Basic
Vocabulary
Builder
Blackline Masters

Русский-English-Español-Français-Deutsch-Italiano-

DOROTHY GABEL LIEBOWITZ

For Teaching
Basic Second-Language Skills
In Various Languages

Illustrated by Judee Levan

National Textbook Company
NTC a division of *NTC Publishing Group* • Lincolnwood, Illinois USA

To the teacher:
    The blackline masters in this book are
designed to be photocopied for classroom
use only.

1994 Printing

PREFACE

For too many years, language teachers have had to prepare their own materials to use for teaching vocabulary. Ironically, as the need for these materials increased, the time available for preparing them decreased. *Basic Vocabulary Builder* resolves this dilemma in that it is a professionally produced, inexpensive, effective timesaver.

Basic Vocabulary Builder is a unique vehicle for teaching and reinforcing basic vocabulary whether the target language is English, Spanish, French, Italian, German, Russian, or Vietnamese. Not only does it provide the teacher with handy worksheets, but it also contains many suggestions for practice and reinforcement as well as games and activities that make learning a second language more fun.

The blackline masters in this book serve as inexpensive learning tools that can be used again and again in a variety of ways for all age groups. These pages of simple illustrations are the building blocks for all kinds of activities that can be tailored to the interests and maturity level of the student. The vocabulary sheets can be used for coloring or writing or for more sophisticated activities like playing vocabulary bingo. When cut out and mounted on heavy paper or cardboard, the illustrations become mini-flash cards for easy review or testing. With a little imagination, the possibilities for using *Basic Vocabulary Builder* are limitless.

The teacher's guide for each blackline master provides vocabulary, grammar, pattern drills, and activities. However, the material in the teacher's guide should serve only as suggestions for launching a creative study of basic vocabulary.

Each lesson contains vocabulary that fits into a particular word group or family. For instance, one lesson covers vocabulary related to the school; another, parts of the body; and another, telling time. Although the lessons are numbered, they may be used in any order.

For more advanced classes, the author has created a companion book entitled *Practical Vocabulary Builder*. Both books are available in either blackline master or spirit master form.

Contents

1. Colors

Vocabulary

English (orange)	Spanish anaranjado, -a: color de naranja (naranja)	French orange (orange)	Italian arancio (arancia)	German orangefarbe (Apfelsine)	Russian оранжевый (апельсин)	Vietnamese màu cam (trái cam)
red (apple)	rojo, -a (manzana)	rouge (pomme)	rosso (mela)	rot (Apfel)	красное (яблоко)	màu đỏ (trái táo)
gray (elephant)	gris (elefante)	gris, -e (éléphant)	grigio (elefante)	grau (Elefant)	серый (слон)	màu xám (con voi)
blue (lake)	azul (lago)	bleu, -e (lac)	azzurro, blu (lago)	blau (See)	синее (озеро)	màu xanh da trời (hồ)
yellow (sun)	amarillo, -a (sol)	jaune (soleil)	giallo (sole)	gelb (Sonne)	жёлтое (солнце)	màu vàng (mặt trời)
white (rabbit)	blanco, -a (conejo)	blanc, blanche (lapin)	bianco (coniglio)	weiss (Kaninchen)	белый (кролик)	màu trắng (con thỏ)
brown (nuts)	café; moreno, -a; castaño, -a; pardo, -a (nueces)	brun, -e (noix)	marrone (noci)	braun (Nuss)	коричневые (орёхи)	màu nâu (hạt dẻ)
green (leaf)	verde (hoja)	vert, -e (feuille)	verde (foglia)	grün (Blatt)	зелёный (лист)	màu xanh lá cây (lá cây)
purple (grapes)	morado, -a; purpúreo, -a (uvas)	violet, violette; pourpre (raisins)	viola (uva)	violett (Traube)	фиолётовый	màu tím (trái nho)
black (cat)	negro, -a (gato)	noir, -e (chat)	nero (gatto)	schwarz (Katze)	чёрный (кот)	màu đen (con mèo)

Vocabulary Supplement apple, leaf, orange, elephant, lake, sun, rabbit, cat, nuts, grapes

Grammar

Concepts: Demonstrative adjectives, Definite articles, Indefinite articles, Negatives
Verbs: to be (is/are), to like

Patterns

1. Point to the object and model the sentence for the students. Have them use the pattern to identify the colors.
   This is a red apple. (green leaf, an orange, gray elephant, blue lake, yellow sun, white rabbit, black cat)
   These are brown nuts. (purple grapes)
   Repeat the above changing to **that** and **those**.
     That is a red apple, etc.
     Those are brown nuts, etc.
2. Change the singular to the plural.
   These are red apples. (green leaves, orange oranges, gray elephants, blue lakes, yellow suns, white rabbits, black cats)
   Change the plural to singular.
     This is a purple grape. (purple grape)
   Repeat the above, changing to **those** and **that**.
     Those are red apples, etc.

   That is a brown nut, etc.
3. Model the pattern for further identification practice.
   I like the yellow sun. (green leaf, gray elephant, blue lake, black cat, orange orange, white rabbit, red apple)
   I like brown nuts. (purple grapes)
   Change the singular to the plural.
     I like yellow suns, etc.
   Change the plural to the singular.
     I like a brown nut, etc.

Activities

1. What color is the orange? (apple, elephant, lake, sun, rabbit, nut, leaf, grape, cat) (The orange is orange.)
   Change the above to the plural.
   What color are oranges? (apples, elephants, etc.) (Oranges are orange.)
2. What do you eat? (I eat an orange, apple, nuts, grapes.)
   Which are animals? (The elephant, cat, rabbit is/are animal/s.)
   How many things do you eat? (four)
   How many are animals? (three)
3. Is an orange red? (No, an orange is not red. It is orange.)
   Is a rabbit blue?
   Is a lake purple?
   Is a nut green?
   Is the sun black?
   Is a leaf brown?
4. What is green? (A leaf is green. Grass is green.) Encourage original responses. Continue with all the colors.
5. Bingo can easily be played using the run-off papers as the boards and beans or pieces of paper for the markers. Because all the boards are the same, numerous players will win at the same time. The true winner can be determined by having the player spell the vocabulary items, give the plural form, give the definite article, give the opposite, a synonym, an antonym, etc.
   Ask the questions from this section numbers 1 or 4 as the clues; the players will cover up the answers. The game can be played horizontally, vertically, four corners, etc.

2. Clothing

Vocabulary

English	Spanish	French	Italian	German	Russian	Vietnamese
shirt	camisa	chemise	camicia	Hemd	рубашка	áo sơ mi
pants	pantalones	pantalon	pantaloni	Hosen	брюки	quần dài tây
shoes	zapatos	chaussures	scarpe	Schuhe	туфли	giày
socks	calcetines, medias	chaussettes	calzini	Socken	носки	vớ, tất
suit	traje	complet	abito	Anzug	костюм	bộ (quần áo)
hat	sombrero	chapeau	cappello	Hut	шляпа	nón, mũ
blouse	blusa	blouse	camicetta	Bluse	блузка	áo bờ lu
skirt	falda	jupe	gonna	Rock	юбка	váy
dress	vestido	robe	vestito	Kleid	платье	áo đầm
sweater	suéter	chandail, pull-over, tricot	golf	Strickjacke, Sweater	свитер	áo ấm, áo len
jacket	chaqueta	veston, jaquette	giacca	Jacke	пиджак	áo khoác
pajamas	pijama, piyama	pyjama	pigiama	Schlafanzug	пижама	bộ áo quần ngủ
bathrobe	bata de baño	robe de chambre	accappatoio	Bademantel	купальный халат	áo choàng tắm
slippers	pantuflas	pantoufles	pantofole	Hausschuhe	тапочки	dép mang trong nhà
underwear	ropa interior	sous-vêtements	biancheria intima	Unterwäsche	нижнее бельё	áo quần lót
coat	abrigo	manteau	cappotto, soprabito	Mantel	пальто	áo choàng

Vocabulary Supplement Colors (1)

Grammar

Concepts: Demonstrative adjectives. Articles.
Noun/adjective agreement
Verbs: to be (is/are), to wear (present tense)

Patterns

1. Point to the object and model the sentence for the students. Have them use the pattern to identify the clothing.
   This is a shirt. (skirt, blouse, underwear, jacket, bathrobe, suit, coat, sweater, dress, hat)
   These are the pants. (pajamas, shoes, socks, slippers)
   Repeat the above changing to **that** and **those.**
   That is a shirt, etc.
   Those are pants, etc.
2. Change the singular to the plural.
   These are shirts, etc.
   Change the plural to the singular.
   This is a shoe, etc.
   Repeat the above, using **that** and **those.**
3. Add a color.
   This is a blue shirt. (red blouse, etc.)
   These are yellow shoes, etc.

4. Complete the sentence with a logical answer.
   A boy wears _____ .
   I am wearing _____ .
   The boys wear _____ .
   You are wearing _____ .
   You (pl.) are wearing _____ .
   We are wearing _____ .

Activities

1. What color is your shirt? (blouse, skirt, etc.)
2. Are you wearing a shirt? (blouse, skirt, etc.)
3. What is _____ (girl's name) wearing?
   What is _____ (boy's name) wearing?
4. Circle the clothing a boy wears.
   Put a line under the clothing a girl wears.
   Put an X through the items you wear on your feet.
5. Color the hat brown, shoes black, underwear white, shirt red, blouse blue, skirt yellow, dress orange, pajamas green.
6. Does your father wear shoes? (suit, socks, skirt, slippers)
   Does your mother wear a blouse? (suit, sweater, slippers, socks)
7. Describe your favorite clothing.

3. Accessories

Vocabulary

English	Spanish	French	Italian	German	Russian	Vietnamese
bathing suit	traje de baño	maillot	costume da bagno	Badeanzug	трусы́, тру́сики	áo tắm
shorts	pantalones cortos	short	pantaloni corti	kurze Hosen	шо́рты, коро́ткие брю́ки	quần tây ngắn
buttons	botones	boutons	bottoni	Knöpfe	пу́товицы	nút
belt	cinturón	ceinture	cintura	Gürtel	по́яс	dây thắt lưng, cái đai
tie	corbata	cravate	cravatta	Schlips; Krawatte	гáлстук	cà vạt
boots	botas	bottes	stivali	Stiefel	сапогѝ, боти́нки	giầy ống, giầy cao cổ
scarf	bufanda	écharpe	sciarpa	Schal	шарф, кашнé	khăn quàng cổ
gloves	guantes	gants	guanti	Handschuhe	перча́тки	bao tay
necklace	collar	collier	collana	Halskette	золотáя, цепóчка	vòng đeo cổ, chuỗi hạt đeo cổ
ring	anillo, sortija	anneau, bague	anello	Ring	кольцó	nhẫn đeo tay
purse	bolsa	sac	borsetta	Handtasche	сýмка	ví đựng tiền (của đàn bà)
wallet	cartera	portefeuille	portafoglio	Portmonnaie, Brieftasche	бумáжник	ví đựng tiền (của đàn ông)
(wrist) watch	reloj (de pulsera)	montre	orologio da polso	Armbanduhr	часы́	đồng hồ đeo tay
umbrella	paraguas, sombrilla	parapluie	ombrello	Regenschirm	зонт	cái ô, cái dù
(eye) glasses	anteojos	lunettes	occhiali	Brille	очки	kính đeo mắt
hairbrush	cepillo	brosse à cheveux	spazzola	Haarbürste	щётка (для волóс)	bàn chải tóc

Vocabulary Supplement Colors (1)

Grammar

Concepts: Noun/adjective agreement, Subject/verb agreement

Verbs: to wear (present tense), to have (present tense)

Patterns

1. Point to the object and model the pattern. Have the students use it to identify the accessories.

   I am wearing a bathing suit. (belt, tie, boots, gloves, necklace, scarf, shorts, glasses, ring)

   You have buttons. (a purse, an umbrella, a watch, a wallet, a hairbrush)

2. Add a color.

   You are wearing a green bathing suit. (belt, tie, boots, umbrella, gloves, scarf, shorts)

   They have red buttons. (a purse, an umbrella, a necklace, glasses, a wallet, a ring,

3. Complete the sentence with a logical answer.

   You wear a ——— in the water. (bathing suit)

   He wears a ——— on his pants. (belt)

   We wear ——— on our feet. (boots)

   I wear ——— on my hands. (gloves, rings)

   They wear a ——— on their neck. (scarf, necklace, tie)

   The boy wears ——— when it's hot. (shorts)

   I have a ——— to tell time. (watch)

   You have a ——— for your money. (wallet, purse)

   We have a ——— for our hair. (hairbrush)

   She has ——— to see. (glasses)

   You (pl.) have ——— on your shirt. (buttons)

   My mother has an ——— for the rain. (umbrella)

Activities

1. What are you (we, they) wearing?
   What is she (he) wearing?
   What am I wearing?

2. Do you have a bathing suit?
   What color is the bathing suit?
   Does your father have a belt?
   What color is the belt?
   Does your mother have boots?
   What color are the boots?
   Do you (pl.) have buttons on your clothes?
   Does ——— (boy's name) have a watch?
   Does ——— (girl's name) have a necklace?
   Do they have a hairbrush?
   Do you have a ring?

3. Do you wear shorts? (they, we, she, he, I, you)

4. Does a boy wear a necklace? (shorts, a watch, etc.)
   Does a girl wear shorts? (a bathing suit, a tie, etc.)

5. What do you do with a hairbrush? (wallet,

6. Circle the items you wear or use on your head. Put a line under the items you wear or use on the arm or hand.
   Draw an X through the items you use when it is raining.

7. Bingo: Read the sentences from Patterns, number 3 as the clues; the players cover up the answers.

8. Play "What am I?"

4. Fruits and Vegetables

Vocabulary

English	Spanish	French	Italian	German	Russian	Vietnamese
apple	manzana	pomme	mela	Apfel	яблоко	trái táo
banana	plátano, banana	banane	banana	Banane	банан	trái chuối
cherry	cereza	cerise	ciliegia	Kirsche	фасоль	trái anh đào
grape	uva	raisin	uva	Weintraube	виноград	trái nho
orange	naranja	orange	arancia	Orange	апельсин	trái cam
lemon	limón	citron	limone	Zitrone	лимон	trái chanh
strawberry	fresa	fraise	fragola	Erdbeere	клубника	trái dâu tây
tomato	tomate	tomate	pomodoro	Tomate	помидор	trái cà chua
lettuce	lechuga	laitue	lattuga	Kopfsalat	салат	cải xà lách
carrot	zanahoria	carotte	carota	Karotte, Mohrrübe	морковь	củ cà rốt
corn	maíz	maïs	granturco	Mais	кукуруза	trái bắp
bean	frijol	haricot	fagiolo	Bohne	фасоль	đậu
pea	chícharo, guisante	petit pois	pisello	Erbse	горох	đậu hột
potato	papa, patata	pomme de terre	patata	Kartoffel	картофель	khoai tây
onion	cebolla	oignon	cipolla	Zwiebel	лук	củ hành tây
pear	pera	poire	pera	Birne	груша	trái lê

Vocabulary Supplement   Colors (1), to grow, next to, to the right of, to the left of, on top of, below

Grammar

Concepts: Subject/verb agreement, Noun/
adjective agreement
Verbs: to eat, to like

Patterns

1. Point to the object and model the pattern.
   Have the students use it to identify the fruit
   and vegetables.
   We eat an apple. (banana, bean, strawberry,
   pear, carrot, orange, pea, potato, tomato,
   lettuce, onion, corn, grape, lemon,
   cherry)
   I like apples. (bananas, beans, strawberries,
   etc.)
2. Following the model, continue with all the
   objects.
   They eat red apples. (yellow bananas, green
   beans, etc.)
   You like green lettuce. (red strawberries,
   green peas, etc.)
3. Complete the sentence with a logical answer.
   I eat a red _____ . (apple, strawberry,
   tomato, cherry)
   You eat a yellow _____ . (banana, pear,
   corn, lemon)
   We eat a green _____ . (bean, pea, lettuce)

They eat an orange _____ . (carrot, orange)
He eats a white _____ . (potato, onion)
You (pl.) eat a purple _____ . (grape)
I like red _____ . (apples, cherries, etc.)
You like yellow _____ . (pears, lemons,
   etc.)
We like green _____ . (peas, beans, etc.)
They like white _____ . (onions, potatoes)
She likes purple _____ . (grapes)

Activities

1. Ask the question, changing the subject.
   Do you eat an apple? (I, they, he, you, she,
   your friend)
   Do you like bananas? (he, they, I, we, you,
   your mother)
2. Where does an apple (pear, orange, lemon,
   cherry, banana) grow? (An apple grows on a
   tree.)
   Where do peas (strawberries, beans, tomatoes,
   corn, grapes) grow? (Peas grow on a
   plant.)
   Where do carrots (potatoes, onions) grow?
   (Carrots grow under the ground.)
3. Reverse the above questions.
   What grows on a tree? (on a plant, under the
   ground)
4. What is next to the peas? (banana, cherry,
   etc.)
   What is to the right of the carrots? (beans,
   corn, etc.)
   What is to the left of the onion? (strawberry,
   cherry, etc.)
   What is on top of the apple? (bean, pea, etc.)
   What is below the potato? (tomato, carrot,
   etc.)
5. How many fruits (vegetables) are there?
6. What is red? (apple, strawberry, tomato,
   cherry)
   What is yellow? (banana, pear, lemon, corn)
   What is purple? (grapes)
   What is green? (peas, beans, lettuce)
   What is orange? (carrot, orange)
   What is brown? (potato)
   What is white? (onion)
7. Bingo: Ask the questions from this section,
   numbers 4 or 6 as clues; the players cover up
   the answers.
8. What fruit (vegetable) would you like to be?
   Why?
9. If you were a carrot and about to be cooked,
   what would your thoughts be? How would
   you try to convince the cook not to do this to
   you?

5. Food—A

Vocabulary

English	Spanish	French	Italian	German	Russian	Vietnamese
meat	carne	viande	carne	Fleisch	мясо	thịt
fish	pescado	poisson	pesce	Fisch	рыба	cá
coffee	café	café	caffè	Kaffee	кофе	cà phê
tea	té	thé	tè	Tee	чай	trà
milk	leche	lait	latte	Milch	молоко	sữa
salad	ensalada	salade	insalata	Salat	салат	rau xà lách
fruit	fruta	fruits	frutta	Obst, Frucht	фрукты	trái cây
pie	pastel	tarte	torta	Obsttorte	пирóг, пирожóк	bánh ngọt có nhân
cake	pastel, torta	gâteau	torta	Kuchen	тóрт, пирóжное	bánh ga tô
cookie	galleta	petit gâteau	pasticcino, biscotto	Plätzchen	печéнье	bánh ngọt nhỏ
bread	pan	pain	pane	Brot	хлеб	bánh mì
fowl	volatería	volaille	volatili	Geflügel	птица	chim, gà, vịt
plate	plato	assiette	piatto	Teller	тарéлка	điã, điã
glass	vaso	verre	bicchiere	Glas	стакáн	ly
knife	cuchillo	couteau	coltello	Messer	нож	dao
fork	tenedor	fourchette	forchetta	Gabel	вилка	cái nĩa
spoon	cuchara	cuiller, cuillère	cucchiaio	Löffel	лóжка	cái muỗng, thìa

Vocabulary Supplement   breakfast, lunch, dinner, dessert, colors, positions

Grammar

Concepts: Subject/verb agreement, Noun/
adjective agreement
Verbs: to eat, to drink, to use

Patterns

1. Point to the object and model the pattern for
   the students. Have them use it to identify the
   food.
   They eat fruit. (bread, meat, fowl, salad, a
   cookie, pie, cake)
   We drink milk. (coffee, tea)
   To eat we use a knife. (fork, spoon, plate,
   glass)
2. Complete the sentence with a logical answer.
   For breakfast I eat _____. (fruit, bread)
   For lunch I eat _____. (meat, fruit, bread)
   For dinner I eat _____. (meat, fish, fowl,
   salad, bread)
   For dessert I eat _____. (cookie, cake, pie)
   I use a _____ to drink milk. (glass)
   I use a _____ to cut meat. (knife)
   I use a _____ to drink hot coffee. (spoon)
   We use a _____ to eat cake. (fork)

3. Change the verb to agree with the new subject.
   I eat fruit. (he, they, we, you, Mary, you [pl.])
   We drink milk. (John, I, you, they, she, you
   [pl.]; we)

Activities

1. Do you (he, we, they, I, she, Joan) eat meat?
2. Do they (he, we, I, she, Joe, the boys) drink
   milk?
3. Do I (he, we, they, she, you, my friends) use
   a knife and fork?
4. What do you eat for breakfast? (lunch,
   dinner, dessert)
5. What do you eat? (drink)
6. What color is meat? (fish, salad, bread, etc.)
7. Does meat (milk, coffee, etc.) grow on a
   tree?
8. What is next to the milk? (meat, fruit, etc.)
   What is on top of the glass? (coffee, bread,
   etc.)
   What is below the salad? (fruit, cake, etc.)
   What is to the right of the bread? (fruit, fish,
   etc.)
   What is to the left of the cookie? (pie, fork,
   etc.)
9. Circle what you would eat for breakfast.
   Put a line under what you would eat for
   dinner.
   Draw an X through what you drink.
10. Bingo: Read the questions from this section.
    number 8 as the clues; the players cover up
    the answers.
11. Make up a menu using the food vocabulary
    already learned.

6. Food—B

Vocabulary

English	Spanish	French	Italian	German	Russian	Vietnamese
steak	biftec, bistec	bifteck	bistecca	Steak	бифштекс	thịt bít tết
hot dog	hot dog, perrito caliente, salchicha	hot-dog	hot dog, salsiccia americana	Wiener(wurst), Frankfurter(wurst)	булочка с горячей сосиской	bánh mì cặp xúc xích
hamburger	hamburguesa	hamburger	hamburger	Hamburger, Frikadelle	рубленый шницель	bánh mì nhét thịt bằm
sandwich	sandwich, emparedado	sandwich	panino imbottito	belegtes Brot	бутерброд	bánh mì săng uých
sausage	salchicha, chorizo	saucisse, saucisson	salsiccia	Wurst	колбаса	thịt xúc xích
salt	sal	sel	sale	Salz	соль	muối
pepper	pimienta	poivre	pepe	Pfeffer	перец	tiêu
egg	huevo	œuf	uovo	Ei	яйцо	trứng
cereal	cereal	céréales	cereale	Getreideflocken	хлопья	mễ cốc
ham	jamón	jambon	prosciutto	Schinken	ветчина	đùi lợn muối, dăm bông
sugar	azúcar	sucre	zucchero	Zucker	сахар	đường
ice cream	helado	glace	gelato	Eis	мороженое	cà rem
candy	bombones, dulces	bonbons	caramella	Bonbons	конфета	kẹo
nuts	nueces	noix	noci	Nüsse	орехи	hạt dẻ
ice	hielo	glace	ghiaccio	Eis	лёд	nước đá
butter	mantequilla	beurre	burro	Butter	масло	bơ
juice	jugo	jus	sugo	Saft	сок	nước trái cây

Vocabulary Supplement   meals, Colors (1), hot, cold

Grammar

Concepts: Subject/verb agreement
Verbs: to eat, to like, to use

Patterns

1. Point to the object and model the pattern for the students. Have them use it to identify the food.
   We like steak. (a hot dog, an egg, salt and pepper, a sandwich, sausage, a hamburger, ham, etc.)
   Change to the plural.
   We like steaks. (hot dogs, eggs, etc.)
2. Complete the sentence with a logical answer.
   We use salt and pepper on _____. (steak, egg, hamburger)
   For breakfast he eats _____. (cereal, sugar, egg)

   For lunch you eat _____. (sandwich, hot dog, sausage, hamburger)
   For dinner I eat _____. (steak, ham, etc.)
   For dessert we eat _____. (ice cream, candy)
3. Change the verb to agree with the new subject.
   We like steak. (I, you |pl.|, she, they, you, my friend, we)
   We like eggs. (I, you |pl.|, she, they, you, your friends, we)
   We like to eat eggs. (I, you, she, they, he, we)

Activities

1. Do you like steak? (she, they, we, he, you |pl.|, your friend)
   Does she like eggs? (hamburger, ham, etc.)
2. What do you eat for breakfast? (lunch, dinner, dessert)
3. Circle the food that is meat.
   Draw a line under the food you eat for dessert.
   Draw an X through the food you eat for breakfast.
4. What color is steak? (a hot dog, salt, pepper, sugar, etc.)
5. What food is hot? (cold)
6. Play "Who am I?" A student gives clues as to the identity of an object; the remaining members of the class try to guess what is being described. The player with the correct answer is the next to give the clues.
7. Plan meals using the food vocabulary.

7. Parts of the Body

Vocabulary

English	Spanish	French	Italian	German	Russian	Vietnamese
head	cabeza	tête	testa. capo	Kopf	голова́	đầu
hair	cabello. pelo	cheveux	capelli	Haar	во́лосы	tóc
eye	ojo	œil, yeux	occhio	Auge	глаз	mặt
nose	nariz	nez	naso	Nase	нос	mũi
mouth	boca	bouche	bocca	Mund	рот	miệng
ear	oreja	oreille	orecchio	Ohr	у́хо	lỗ tai
arm	brazo	bras	braccio	Arm	рука́	cánh tay
finger	dedo	doigt	dito	Finger	па́лец	ngón tay
leg	pierna	jambe	gamba	Bein	ступня́	cái chân
foot	pie	pied	piede	Fuß	нога́	bàn chân
chest	pecho	poitrine	petto	Brust	грудь	ngực
knee	rodilla	genou	ginocchio	Knie	коле́но	đầu gối
back	espalda	dos	schiena	Rücken	спина́	lưng
throat (neck)	garganta (cuello)	gorge (cou)	gòla (collo)	Rachen (Hals)	го́рло (ше́я)	cuống họng (cổ)
elbow	codo	coude	gomito	Ellbogen	ло́коть	khuỷu tay
hand	mano	main	mano	Hand	рука́	bàn tay

Vocabulary Supplement numbers 1, 2, 10; to run, smell, read, talk, walk, breathe, play, swim, watch; positions

Grammar

Concepts: Subject/verb agreement
Verbs: to have, to use

Patterns

1. Point to the object and model the pattern for the students. Have them use it to identify the parts of the body.

   I have one head. (two eyes, one nose, two arms, two legs, much hair, two ears, one mouth, ten fingers, one chest, two feet, two hands, two elbows, one back, one throat, two knees)

   You have one _____. (head, nose, throat, mouth, chest, back)

   They have two _____. (eyes, arms, legs, ears, feet, hands, elbows, knees)

   We have much _____. (hair)

   He has ten _____. (fingers)

2. Complete the sentence with a logical answer.

   To run I use _____. (legs, feet, knees)

   To eat he uses _____. (head, arms, mouth, fingers, hands, throat)

   To see we use _____. (eyes)

   To smell we use _____. (nose)

3. Change the verb to agree with the new subject. (you, we, they, you [pl.], she,

   the boys, he)

   I use two eyes. (you, we, they, you [pl.], she, the girls, he)

Activities

1. How many eyes do you have? (noses, legs, heads, etc.)
2. For what do you use eyes? (nose, arms, legs, etc.)
3. Circle the things you have one of. Draw a line under the things you have two of. Draw an X through the things you have ten of.
4. What do you use to read? (talk, see, walk, smell, eat, breathe, play baseball, swim, watch television)
5. What is next to the mouth? (eyes, back, etc.) What is on top of the ear? (hair, elbow, finger, etc.)

   What is below the leg? (nose, hand, etc.)
   What is to the right of the ear? (head, chest, etc.)
   What is to the left of the eyes? (hand, neck, etc.)
6. Bingo: Read the clues; the players cover up the items associated with the clues.

to see	(eyes)	to think	(head)
to touch	(hands, finger)	to bend	(knee, elbow)
to smell	(nose)	to brush	(hair)
to swallow	(neck)	to breathe	(chest)
to run	(leg, foot)		
to talk	(mouth)		
to hear	(ear)		

8. The Family

Vocabulary

English	Spanish	French	Italian	German	Russian	Vietnamese
mother	madre	mère	mamma, madre	Mutter	мать	má, mẹ
father	padre	père	papà, padre	Vater	отéц	cha, bố
husband	esposo, marido	mari, époux	marito	Ehemann, Gatte	муж	chồng
wife	esposa, señora	femme, épouse	moglie	Ehefrau, Gattin	женá	vợ
daughter	hija	fille	figlia	Tochter	дочь	con gái
son	hijo	fils	figlio	Sohn	сын	con trai
sister	hermana	sœur	sorella	Schwester	сестрá	chị gái, em gái
brother	hermano	frère	fratello	Bruder	брат	anh trai, em trai
grandfather	abuelo	grand-père	nonno	Großvater	дéдушка	ông nội, ông ngoại
grandmother	abuela	grand-mère	nonna	Großmutter	бáбушка	bà nội, bà ngoại
granddaughter	nieta	petite-fille	nipote	Enkelin	внучка	cháu nội gái, cháu ngoại gái
grandson	nieto	petit-fils	nipote	Enkel	внук	cháu nội trai, cháu ngoại trai
aunt	tía	tante	zia	Tante	тётя	dì, cô, bác
uncle	tío	oncle	zio	Onkel	дядя	cậu, chú, bác
niece	sobrina	nièce	nipote	Nichte	племянница	cháu gái
nephew	sobrino	neveu	nipote	Neffe	племянник	cháu trai
cousin	primo, prima	cousin, cousine	cugino, -a	Cousin, Cousine	двоюродный брат, двоюродная сестрá	anh chị em họ hàng

Vocabulary Supplement oldest, youngest

Grammar

Concepts: Subject/verb agreement
Verbs: to have, to be (is)

Patterns

1. Point to the object and model the pattern for
   the students. Have them use it to identify the
   members of a family.
   I have a mother. (father, sister, etc.)
2. Complete the pair.
   father ――― (mother)
   daughter ――― (son)
   wife ――― (husband)
   brother ――― (sister)
   aunt ――― (uncle)
   grandmother ――― (grandfather)
   niece ――― (nephew)
3. Complete the sentence with a logical answer.
   A woman can be a ――― . (mother,
   daughter, wife, cousin, sister, aunt, grandmother, granddaughter, niece)

   A man can be a ――― . (father, son,
   husband, cousin, brother, uncle, grandfather, grandson, nephew)
4. Complete the sentences.
   My mother's mother is my ―――.
   (grandmother)
   My father's father is my ―――.
   (grandfather)
   My mother's son is my ―――.
   (brother)
   My mother's daughter is my ―――.
   (sister)
   My mother's sister is my ―――.
   (aunt)
   My mother's brother is my ―――.
   (uncle)
   My aunt's son is my ―――.
   (cousin)
   My uncle's daughter is my ―――.
   (cousin)

Activities

1. Do you have a mother? (he, they, we, you
   [pl.], she)
2. Do you have a sister? (brother, aunt, etc.)
3. How many sisters do you have? (brothers,
   cousins, aunts, uncles)
4. Who is the oldest? (youngest)
5. What is your mother's name? (father's,
   brother's, etc.)
6. How old are you? (is your mother, father, etc.)
7. Draw your own family tree.

9. Miscellaneous

Vocabulary

English	Spanish	French	Italian	German	Russian	Vietnamese
man	hombre	homme	uomo	Mann	мужчина	đàn ông
woman	mujer, dama	femme	donna	Frau	жéнщина	đàn bà
boy	muchacho, niño	garçon	ragazzo	Junge, Knabe	мáльчик	con trai
girl	muchacha, niña	jeune fille	ragazza	Mädchen	дéвочка	con gái
teenager	adolescente	adolescent, adolescente	adolescente	Jugendlicher, Jugendliche	подрóсток	vị thành niên
old	viejo, -a	vieux, vieille; âgé, -e	vecchio	alt	стáрый	già, lớn tuổi
young	joven	jeune	giovane	jung	молодóй	trẻ
baby	bebé, bebito, bebita, nene	bébé, enfant	bambino, -a	Baby	ребёнок	em bé
short	bajo, -a; pequeño, -a	petit, -e	basso, -a	kurz	низкий	thấp, nhỏ
tall	alto, -a	grand, -e	alto, -a	lang, groß	высóкий	cao, lớn
fat	gordo, -a	gros, -se	grasso, -a	dick	тóлстый	mập, béo
thin	delgado, -a	maigre	magro, -a	dünn	худóй	ốm, gầy, mảnh mai
big	grande	grand, -e	grande	groß	большóй	to, lớn
small	pequeño, -a	petit, -e	piccolo, -a	klein	мáленький	nhỏ, bé
pretty	bonito, -a, lindo, -a; hermoso, -a	joli, -e; beau, belle	carino, -a	hübsch, schön	красивый	xinh xắn, đẹp
ugly	feo, -a	laid, -e	brutto, -a	häßlich	некрасивый	xấu xí

Vocabulary Supplement   none

Grammar

Concepts: Noun/adjective agreement
Verbs: to be (is/are)

Patterns

1. Point to the object and model the pattern for the students. Have them use it to identify the objects.
   My father is a man. (mother-woman, sister-girl, brother-boy, sister-teenager, grandfather-old man, brother-young man, baby-young)
   The flower is short. (tall)
   The woman is fat. (thin)
   The fish is big. (small)
   The woman is pretty. (man-ugly)
2. Complete the sentence with a logical answer.
   The _____ is short. (girl, boy, teenager, baby, flower, mouse)
3. Change the sentence to agree with the new subject.
   The man is fat. (woman, boy, girl, baby)
   The flowers are ugly. (women, men, animals, babies, girls, boys)

Activities

1. Are you short? (tall)
   Are you fat? (thin)
   Are you big? (small)
   Are you pretty? (ugly)
2. Is _____ (boy's name) short? (tall, fat, thin, big, small, pretty, ugly)
   Is _____ (girl's name) short? (tall, thin, fat, big, small, pretty, ugly)
3. Who is tall? (short)
   What things are tall? (short)
   What things are fat? (thin)
   What things are small? (large)
   What things are pretty? (ugly)
4. Who do you look like? (your mother, father, brother, sister, etc.)
5. Bingo: Read off the clues; the players cover up the opposites to win.
   woman (man)   ugly (pretty)
   pretty (ugly)   man (woman)

girl (boy)
old (young)
fat (thin)
big (little)
tall (short)

short (tall)
boy (girl)
thin (fat)
little (big)
young (old)

10. Health

Vocabulary

English	Spanish	French	Italian	German	Russian	Vietnamese
to be fine (healthy)	estar bien (de salud)	aller bien, être en bonne santé	stare bene	gesund zu sein	здоров	khoẻ mạnh
sick	enfermo, -a	malade	malato, -a	krank	болен	đau ốm
cold	resfriado	rhume	raffreddore	Erkältung	простуда	cảm cúm
medicine	medicina, medicamento	médicament	medicina	Medizin	лекáрство	thuốc men
fever	fiebre	fièvre	febbre	Fieber	жар	nóng, sốt
bandage	vendaje	pansement	fascia	Binde, Verband	бинт	băng vải
headache	dolor de cabeza, jaqueca	mal de tête	mal di testa	Kopfschmerzen	болит головá	nhức đầu
cut	cortada, cortadura	blessure	taglio	Schnitt	порéз	vết thương
blood	sangre	sang	sangue	Blut	кровь	máu
pill	pastilla, píldora, tableta	comprimé, pilule	pillola	Pille	пилюля	thuốc viên
shot	inyección	injection, piqûre	puntura	Spritze	укóл	chích thuốc
sore throat	mal de garganta	mal à la gorge	mal di gola	Halsschmerzen; Halsweh	ангина	đau cổ họng
stomachache	dolor de estómago	mal à l'estomac	mal di stomaco	Magenschmerzen	болит живóт	đau bụng
heart	corazón	cœur	cuore	Herz	сéрдце	tim
bone	hueso	os	osso	Knochen	кость	xương
toothache	dolor de diente	mal aux dents	mal di denti	Zahnschmerz	болит зуб	nhức răng

Vocabulary Supplement   none

Grammar

Concepts: Subject/verb agreement
Verbs: to have

Patterns

1. Point to the object and model the pattern for the students. Have them use it to identify the objects.

   I am fine. (sick)
   You have a cold. (pill, fever, medicine, etc.)

2. Have the students refer to the pictures to complete the sentence.

   My _____ hurts me. (b)

   b. head, stomach
   c. nose, head
   g. head
   h. finger
   j. arm
   l. stomach
   k. throat
   o. mouth, tooth

3. Change the verb to agree with the new subject.
   I am fine. (you, he, she, they, we, the girls, you [pl.], I)
   My head hurts me. (fingers, leg, foot, stomach, throat, elbows, knees, head, nose, legs)
   Her fingers hurt her. (repeat above)

Activities

1. How are you? (your brother, father, sister, mother)
2. Point to different parts of your body and have the students identify them, saying:
   My head hurts me. My legs hurt me, etc.
3. Referring to the pictures indicated, answer the questions.
   How is the boy? (a, b, c, e, k)
   How is the girl? (g, l, o)
4. What do you do when you have a cold? (fever, headache, cut, sore throat, stomachache, toothache)
5. Circle how you feel today.
   Underline how you felt yesterday.
6. You are a doctor; prescribe remedies for the following: headache, sore throat, fever, stomachache, toothache, cold, broken bone, a bleeding cut.

11. Activities

Vocabulary

English	Spanish	French	Italian	German	Russian	Vietnamese
to stand (up)	levantarse	se lever	alzarsi	aufstehen	стоя́ть, встава́ть	đứng (lên)
to sit (down)	sentarse	s'asseoir	sedersi	sitzen	сиде́ть, сади́ться	ngồi xuống
to lie down	acostarse	se coucher	coricarsi	legen	лежа́ть, ложи́ться	nằm xuống
to walk	andar, caminar, ir a pie, marchar, pasear(se)	aller à pied, marcher, se promener	camminare	laufen	идти́	đi bộ
to jump	brincar, saltar	sauter, bondir	saltare	springen	пры́гать	nhảy
to sleep	dormir	dormir	dormire	schlafen	спать	ngủ
to eat	comer	manger, prendre	mangiare	essen	есть	ăn
to run	correr	courir	correre	rennen	бежа́ть, бе́гать	chạy
to play	jugar, tocar	jouer à, de	giocare	spielen	игра́ть	chơi đùa
to wash (oneself)	lavarse	se laver	lavarsi	(sich) waschen	мы́ться	lau, rửa
to write	escribir	écrire	scrivere	schreiben	писа́ть	viết
to read	leer	lire	leggere	lesen	чита́ть	đọc
to study	estudiar	étudier	studiare	studieren	занима́ться	học
to carry	llevar, traer, cargar	porter	portare	tragen	нести́, носи́ть	xách, mang
to climb	escalar, subir, trepar	monter	salire, arrampicarsi	klettern	влеза́ть	trèo, leo
to talk	hablar, charlar	parler, bavarder	parlare	sprechen	говори́ть	nói chuyện

Vocabulary Supplement morning, afternoon, night

Grammar

Concepts: Subject/verb agreement
Verbs: to have to, to go to

Patterns

1. Point to the object and model the pattern for the students. Have them use it to identify the activities.

   I have to stand up. (sit down, lie down, etc.)
   She has to stand up. (sit down, lie down, etc.)
   He has to stand up. (sit down, lie down, etc.)

2. Complete the sentences by referring to the pictures indicated.

   I am going to _____. (a, b, c, etc.)
   We have to _____. (a, b, c, etc.)
   The girl has to _____. (a, b, c, e, i, p)
   The boys have to _____. (f, h, j, l, m, n)
   We are going to _____. (d, g, l, h, b, f)
   You are going to _____. (a, c, f, p, m, i)

Activities

1. Answer the questions, using any of the activities.
   What does she have to do? (he, they, we, the man, the woman, I, you)

2. Referring to the pictures indicated, answer the questions.
   What is the woman doing? (d)
   What is the girl doing? (a, c, e, i, k, p)
   What is the boy doing? (f, h, j, l, m, o)
   When do you sit down? (walk. run. eat. etc.)
   Do you have to eat? (he, you |pl.|, we, they, I)

3. Circle what you do in the morning.

4. Draw a line under what you do in the afternoon.
   Draw an X through what you do at night.

5.

6. Bingo: Read the clues; the players cover up the answers. To win, ask the players to give the verb or to conjugate it in the present tense.

   I am dirty. (j)
   I am hungry. (g)
   I am tired. (f)
   I have a test in mathematics. (m)
   The telephone rang. (p)
   _____ at the race. (h)

   A bear is chasing me. (o)
   I am at the library. (l)
   I am helping my mother. (n)
   I am not sitting or lying down. (a)
   I have a rope. (e)
   I am using a pencil. (k)
   I am using my two legs. (d)
   I am not standing or lying down. (b)
   I am not sitting or standing. (c)
   I have my toys. (i)

12. Sports and Recreation

Vocabulary

English	Spanish	French	Italian	German	Russian	Vietnamese
basketball	baloncesto, básquetbol	basketball	pallacanestro	Basketball, Korbballspiel	баскетбол	bóng rổ
tennis	tenis	tennis	tennis	Tennis	тённис	quần vợt
baseball	beisbol	base-ball	base ball	Baseball(spiel)	бейсбол	bóng cầu
golf	golf	golf	golf	Golfspiel	гольф	gôn
(to) ice-skate	patinar	patiner	pattinare	schlittschuhlaufen	кататься на коньках	trượt nước đá
(to) ride horseback	montar a caballo	monter à cheval	cavalcare	reiten	ехать верхом	cưỡi ngựa
(to) fish	pescar	pêcher	pescare	fischen	ловить рыбу	câu cá
(to) swim	nadar	nager	nuotare	schwimmen	плавать	bơi lội
volleyball	volibol	volleyball	pallavolo	Volleyball	волейбол	bóng chuyền
soccer	futbol	football	calcio	Fußballspiel	футбол	đá banh, túc cầu
photography	fotografía	photographie	fotografia	Photographie	фотография	chụp hình, nhiếp ảnh
(to) sail	navegar, velar	faire de la voile	navigare	segeln	идти под парусами	kéo buồm
boxing	boxeo	boxe	pugilato	Boxen, Boxsport	бокс	quyền thuật
(to) ski (snow)	esquiar	faire du ski	sciare (neve)	skilaufen	ходить на лыжах	trượt tuyết
(to) ski (water)	esquiar en el agua	faire du ski nautique	sciare (acqua)	wasserskilaufen	кататься на (водных) лыжах	trượt nước
(to) hike	caminar	faire une excursion à pied	fare un'escursione a piedi, fare una camminata	wandern	идти (ходить) в туристический поход	cuộc đi bộ

Vocabulary Supplement   to play, winter, summer, to need

Grammar

Concepts: Subject/verb agreement
Verbs: to like (to)

Patterns

1. Point to the object and model the pattern for the students. Have them use it to identify the sports.
   I like to play basketball. (tennis, baseball, golf, volleyball, soccer)
   We like to ice skate. (to ride horseback, to fish, to swim, to photograph, to sail, to box, to ski, to hike)
2. Complete the sentences with a logical answer.
   In the winter he likes to _____. (ice skate, ski)
   In the summer she likes to _____. (remaining items)
   To play _____ I need a ball. (basketball, tennis, baseball, volleyball, soccer)
   I need water to _____. (ice skate, fish, swim, sail, water ski)
3. Complete the sentences by referring to the indicated pictures.
   The boy likes to _____. (c, a, h, d, j, p, m, o, n, g)
   The girl likes to _____. (i, l, k, b, e, f)

Activities

1. Do you like to play baseball? (he, they, I, you [pl.], she, we)
2. What do you like to do in the winter? (in the summer)
3. For which sports do you need water? For which sports do you need a ball?
4. Referring to the pictures, answer the questions. What does the boy like to do? (c, a, h, d, j, p, m, o, n, g) What does the girl like to do? (i, l, k, e, b, f)
5. Circle the things you can do in the winter. Draw a line under the things you can do in the summer. Draw an X through the things you cannot do alone.
6. Do you play basketball? (tennis, baseball, golf, soccer, volleyball) Do you ride a horse? (fish, swim, ski, hike)
7. What is your favorite sport? Why?
8. Bingo: Read the clues; the players cover up the answers. To win, ask the players to give the verb or to conjugate it in a tense.
   - camera (k)
   - horse (f)
   - gloves (m)
   - pole (g)
   - "Babe" Ruth or bat, ball (c)
   - Mark Spitz (h)
   - ice (e)
   - boat (l)
   - club, ball (d)
   - Pelé or round ball, net, kick (j)
   - water (o)
   - ball, racket (b)
   - round ball, basket, throw (a)
   - snow (n)

13. Numbers

Vocabulary

English	Spanish	French	Italian	German	Russian	Vietnamese
one	uno, un, una	un, une	uno	eins	один, одна, одно	một
two	dos	deux	due	zwei	два, две	hai
three	tres	trois	tre	drei	три	ba
four	cuatro	quatre	quattro	vier	четыре	bốn
five	cinco	cinq	cinque	fünf	пять	năm
six	seis	six	sei	sechs	шесть	sáu
seven	siete	sept	sette	sieben	семь	bảy
eight	ocho	huit	otto	acht	восемь	tám
nine	nueve	neuf	nove	neun	девять	chín
ten	diez	dix	dieci	zehn	десять	mười
fifteen	quince	quinze	quindici	fünfzehn	пятнадцать	mười lăm
twenty-three	veinitrés (veinte y tres)	vingt-trois	ventitré	dreiundzwanzig	двадцать три	hai mươi ba
four hundred	cuatrocientos, -as	quatre cents	quattrocento	vierhundert-	четыреста	bốn trăm
six thousand	seis mil	six mille	sei mila	sechstausend	шесть тысяч	sáu ngàn
one thousand nine hundred eighty-four	mil ochocientos ochenta y cuatro	mille neuf cent quatre-vingt-quatre	millenovecento ottantaquattro	eintausendneun-hundertvierund-achtzig	тысяча девятьсот восемьдесят четыре	một ngàn chín trăm tám mươi bốn
eight million	ocho millones	huit millions	otto milioni	acht millionen	восемь миллионов	tám triệu
two-thirds	dos tercios	deux troisièmes	due terzi	zwei drittel	две третьих	hai phần ba
three-fourths	tres cuartos	trois quatrièmes	tre quarti	drei viertel	три четвёртых	ba phần tư

Vocabulary Supplement   Numbers to 100, hundreds

Grammar

Concepts: Subject/verb agreement
Verbs: to be (is/are)

Patterns

1. Identify the numbers by counting in sequence. Reinforce by counting backwards. (by 2's)
2. Introduce the numbers 11-20, combinations after twenty, hundreds, etc.
3. Complete the problems.
   Two and one are ——. (three)
   Three and two are ——. (five)
   Four and three are ——. (seven)
   Six and two are ——. (eight)
   Five and four are ——. (nine)
   One and zero are ——. (one)
   Three and one are ——. (four)
   One and one are ——. (two)
   Four and two are ——. (six)
   Six and four are ——. (ten)
4. Change the above problems to subtraction.
   Two minus one is ——. (one)
   Three minus two is ——. (one)

Activities

1. Addition
   One and one are ——. (one and two.
      three, four, etc.)
   Two and one are ——. (two and two,
      three, four, etc.)
   Three and one are ——. (three and two,
      three, four, etc.)
   Four and one are ——. (three and two,
      three, four, etc.)
   Continue with numbers to ten.
2. Subtraction
   Ten minus one is ——. (ten minus two.
      three, four, etc.)
   Nine minus one is ——. (nine minus two.
      three, four, etc.)
   Eight minus one is ——. (eight minus
      two, three, four, etc.)
3. Continue with numbers to one.
4. Count by tens to one hundred.
5. Count by hundreds to one thousand.
6. Count by fives to one hundred.
7. Count by thousands.
   What year is it?
   What year were you born?
8. Add all the numbers together. Subtract the smallest from the largest.
9. Bingo: Read the clues; the players cover up the answers.
   three plus one equals ——. (four)
   nineteen eighty plus four equals ——. (nineteen eighty-four)
   five plus two equals ——. (seven)
   nine million minus one million equals ——. (eight million)
   eight minus seven equals ——. (one)
   fifteen plus eight equals ——. (twenty-three)
   sixteen minus seven equals ——. (nine)
   one multiplied by two equals ——. (two)
   twenty-five divided by five equals ——. (five)
   five multiplied by three equals ——. (fifteen)
   two plus one equals ——. (three)
   twelve thousand divided by thirty equals ——. (four hundred)
   two multiplied by three equals ——. (six)
   sixteen divided by two equals ——. (eight)
   five multiplied by two equals ——. (ten)
   ten thousand minus four thousand equals ——. (six thousand)

14. Telling Time

Vocabulary

English	Spanish	French	Italian	German	Russian	Vietnamese
twelve o'clock (noon)	mediodía	midi	mezzogiorno	Mittag	двенадцать часов (полдень)	mười hai giờ (trưa)
twelve o'clock (midnight)	medianoche	minuit	mezzanotte	Mitternacht	двенадцать часов (полночь)	mười hai giờ (đêm)
three o'clock	las tres	trois heures	Sono le tre	drei Uhr	три часá	ba giờ
ten o'clock	las diez	dix heures	Sono le dieci	zehn Uhr	дéсять часóв	mười giờ
five forty-five	seis menos cuarto	six heures moins (le) quart	Sono le sei meno un quarto	viertel vor sechs	без чéтверти шесть	năm giờ bốn lăm
four thirty	cuatro y media	quatre heures et demie	Sono le quattro e mezzo	halb fünf	половина пятого	bốn giờ ba mươi
ten after three	tres y diez	trois heures dix	Sono le tre e dieci	zehn (Minuten) nach drei	дéсять минýт четвёртого	ba giờ mười
twelve thirty	doce y media	midi (minuit) et demi	Sono le dodici e mezzo	halb eins	половина пéрвого	mười hai giờ ba mươi
one twenty	una y veinte	une heure vingt	È l'una e venti	zwanzig nach eins	двáдцать минýт вторóго	một giờ hai mươi
four thirty-five	cinco menos veinticinco (veinte y cinco)	cinq heures moins vingt-cinq	Sono le cinque meno venticinque	fünfundzwanzig (Minuten) vor fünf	без двадцати пятú пять	bốn giờ ba mươi lăm
five to nine	nueve menos cinco	neuf heures moins cinq	Sono le nove meno cinque	fünf (Minuten) vor neun	без пятú дéвять	chín giờ thiếu năm
eight fifteen	ocho y cuarto	huit heures et quart	Sono le otto e un quarto	viertel nach acht	чéтверть девятого	tám giờ mười lăm
five after twelve	doce y cinco	midi (minuit) cinq	Sono le dodici e cinque	fünf (Minuten) nach zwölf	пять минýт пéрвого	mười hai giờ lẻ năm
twenty to eleven	once menos veinte	onze heures moins vingt	Sono le undici meno venti	zwanzig (Minuten) vor elf	без двадцати одиннадцать	mười một giờ thiếu hai mươi
seven twenty-five	siete y veinticinco (veinte y cinco)	sept heures vingt-cinq	Sono le sette e venticinque	fünfundzwanzig (Minuten) nach sieben	двáдцать пять минýт восьмóго	bảy giờ hai mươi lăm
ten to two	dos menos diez	deux heures moins dix	Sono le due meno dieci	zehn (Minuten) vor zwei	без десятú два	hai giờ thiếu mười

Vocabulary Supplement   Numbers (13)

14. Telling Time, cont'd

Grammar

Concepts: Telling time
Verbs: to be (is/are)

Patterns

1. Point to the clocks and model the pattern for the students. Have them use it to identify the times.

   It's twelve o'clock. (It's noon, midnight, three o'clock, etc.)

2. Complete the sentence with a logical response.
   I get up in the morning at _____.
   I eat breakfast at _____.
   I go to school at _____.
   I eat lunch at _____.
   I leave school at _____.
   I play at _____.
   I study at _____.
   I eat dinner at _____.
   I watch television at _____.
   I go to bed at _____.

3. Add ten minutes to each clock. (It's twelve ten, three ten, etc.)

4. Subtract fifteen minutes from each clock. (It's eleven forty-five, it's two forty-five, etc.)

Activities

1. Referring to the clocks, answer the questions.
   What time is it? (a through p)
   What do you do at _____?' (a through p)

2. What time do you get up in the morning?
   What time do you eat breakfast?
   What time do you go to school?
   What time do you eat lunch? (leave school, play, study, eat dinner, watch television, go to bed)

3. What do you do at noon? (at midnight)

4. What do you do at eight in the morning? (three in the afternoon, eight at night)

5. Bingo: Add ten minutes on to the times on the clocks. Add ten minutes on to the times on the clocks subtract the ten minutes and cover up the correct clock. To win, the players must be able to give the correct times on the clocks.

   It is ten fifty.   (n)
   It is three ten.   (c)
   It is eight twenty-five.   (l)
   It is five fifty-five.   (e)
   It is twelve forty.   (h)
   It is two o'clock.   (p)
   It is twelve ten P.M.   (a)
   It is ten ten.   (d)
   It is three twenty.   (g)
   It is four forty-five.   (j)
   It is twelve ten A.M.   (b)
   It is one thirty.   (i)
   It is four forty.   (f)
   It is 9:05.   (k)
   It is twelve fifteen.   (m)
   It is seven thirty-five.   (o)

15. Shapes and Containers

Vocabulary

English	Spanish	French	Italian	German	Russian	Vietnamese
square	cuadrado	carré	quadrato	Quadrat, Viereck	квадра́т	hình vuông
circle	círculo	cercle	circolo	Kreis	круг	hình tròn
semicircle	semicírculo	demi-cercle	semicircolo	Halbkreis	полукру́г	nửa hình tròn
oval	óvalo	ovale	ovale	Oval	ова́л	hình bầu dục
triangle	triángulo	triangle	triangolo	Dreieck	треуго́льник	hình tam giác
crescent	creciente	croissant	crescente, a mezzaluna	Halbmond	полукру́г	hình bán nguyệt
diamond	rombo, diamante	losange, diamant	diamante	Raute, Diamant	алма́з	hình thoi
cone	cono	cône	cono	Kegel	ко́нус	hình nón
rectangle	rectángulo	rectangle	rettangolo	Rechteck	прямоуго́льник	hình chữ nhật
box (carton)	caja (cartón)	boîte (carton)	scatola (scatola di cartone)	Schachtel, Karton	коро́бка	hộp (thùng)
can	lata	boîte	barattolo	Büchse, Dose	(консéрвная) бáнка	lon
bottle	botella, frasco	bouteille	bottiglia	Flasche	буты́лка	chai
jar	frasco, jarra, jarro	jarre, vase	vaso	Krug	(стекля́нная) бáнка	keo, hũ
bag	saco	sac	sacco	Tüte	бумáжный мешóк	túi xách
bowl (lid)	cuenco, escudilla (la tapa)	bol (couvercle)	scodella (coperchio)	Schale, Schüssel (Deckel)	мúска (кры́шка)	tô (nắp)
pail	cubo, balde	seau	secchio	Eimer	ведрó	cái xô

Vocabulary Supplement   common objects

Grammar

Concepts: Demonstrative adjectives, Noun/ adjective agreement
Verbs: to be (is/are)

Patterns

1. Point to the object and model the pattern for the students. Have them use it to identify the shapes and containers.
   This is a circle. (square, oval, etc.)
   That is a small circle. (square, oval, etc.)
   Change the above to the plural.
   These are circles. (squares, ovals, etc.)
   Those are small circles. (squares, ovals, etc.)

2. Complete the sentences with a logical answer.
   An egg is an _____ . (oval)
   The sun is a _____ . (circle)
   The moon is a _____ . (circle, half circle, crescent)
   A _____ has three sides. (triangle)
   A _____ has four sides. (square, rectangle, diamond)
   A _____ has points. (square, triangle, diamond, cone, etc.)
   A _____ is made of paper. (box, bag)
   Soft drinks come in a _____ . (can, bottle)
   Water is in the _____ . (pail)
   Food is in the _____ . (bowl, jar, can)
   Mustard is in the _____ . (jar)

3. Give the shape for the following items:

sun	pail	box
bag	moon	egg
bottle	can	jar
kite	ball	ice cream
package	bowl	cone

4. What can you put into the following things?
   pail, box, jar, can, bag, bowl, bottle

5. What would you put these items into?
   nuts, water, groceries, apples, cookies, milk, corn, candy, a present, paint, ketchup

Activities

1. Name an object which has the following shapes:
   circle, square, oval, triangle, rectangle, half circle, diamond, cone.

2. Bingo: Read the clues; the players cover up the answers.

egg	(oval)
brown paper	(bag)
box	(square)
sun	(circle)
moon	(crescent)
water	(pail)
ice cream	(cone)
3 sides	(triangle)
made of metal	(can)
made of glass	(bottle, jar)
4 sides	(square, rectangle)
a ring	(diamond, circle)
half of a cookie	(half circle)

16. The House

Vocabulary

English	Spanish	French	Italian	German	Russian	Vietnamese
living room	sala, salón	living, salon	salotto	Wohnzimmer	гостúная	phòng khách
dining room	comedor	salle à manger	sala da pranzo	Speisezimmer	столóвая	phòng ăn
kitchen	cocina	cuisine	cucina	Küche	кýхня	nhà bếp
bedroom	alcoba, dormitorio, recámara	chambre à coucher	camera da letto	Schlafzimmer	спáльня	phòng ngủ
bathroom	cuarto de baño	salle de bains	stanza da bagno	Badezimmer	вáнная	phòng tắm
roof	techo, tejado	toit	tetto	Dach	крýша	mái nhà
floor	piso, suelo	plancher	pavimento	Fußboden	пол	sàn nhà
wall	pared	mur	parete	Wand	стенá	vách tường
door	puerta	porte	porta	Tür	дверь	cửa lớn
closet	armario, gabinete	armoire, cabinet	armadio	Schrank	стеннóй шкáф	phòng nhỏ
window	ventana	fenêtre	finestra	Fenster	окнó	cửa sổ
patio (yard)	patio	patio (cour)	cortile	Terrasse (Hof)	двóрик	sân sau
stairs	escalera	escalier	scale	Treppe	лéстница	thang lầu
garage	garaje	garage	garage	Garage	гарáж	nhà xe
elevator	ascensor, elevador	ascenseur	ascensore	Aufzug	лифт	thang máy
balcony	balcón	balcon	balcone	Balkon	балкóн	sân thượng

Vocabulary Supplement Activities (11)

Grammar

Concepts: There is/are
Verbs: Present tense

Patterns

1. Point to the object and model the pattern for the students. Have them use it to identify the parts of the house.

   There is/are a _____ in the house.
   (bedroom, roof, closet, etc.)

2. Complete the sentences.

   I sit down to read in the _____. (living room, bedroom)
   I walk up and down _____. (stairs)
   I eat in the _____. (dining room, kitchen)
   I look through a _____. (window)
   I wash myself in the _____. (bathroom)
   I sleep in the _____. (bedroom)
   I go up and down in an _____. (elevator)
   The car is in the _____. (garage)
   I cook in the _____. (kitchen)
   Pictures are on the _____. (wall)
   I walk on the _____. (floor)
   I have clothes in the _____. (closet)
   I come into a house through the _____.

   The top of the house is the _____. (roof)
   I play outside in/on the _____. (patio, yard)

Activities

1. Is there a bathroom in (on) the house? (bedroom, roof, closet, etc.)
2. How many bathrooms are there in your house? (bedrooms, closets, etc.)
3. Where do you read? (eat, wash yourself, sleep, cook, put your clothes, play)
4. Draw your house and label the rooms.
5. What do you do in the bathroom? (kitchen, bedroom, dining room, living room, garage, yard/patio, elevator)
6. Bingo: Read the sentences from Patterns, number 2 as the clues; the players cover up the answers.

17. Furnishings

Vocabulary

English	Spanish	French	Italian	German	Russian	Vietnamese
couch (sofa)	sofá	canapé, divan, sofa	divano (sofà)	Sofa	диван	ghế dài
chair	silla	chaise, fauteuil	sedia	Stuhl	стул	ghế
lamp	lámpara	lampe	lampada	Lampe	лампа	đèn
table	mesa	table	tavola	Tisch	стол	bàn
bed	cama	lit	letto	Bett	кровать	giường
dresser (bureau)	cómoda, tocador	armoire, dressoir	comò (cassettone)	Kommode	комод	bàn trang điểm
sink	fregadero, pila	évier, lavabo	lavandino	Waschbecken, Spülstein	раковина	chậu rửa chén bát
stove	estufa, fogón	cuisinière	stufa	Ofen, Herd	плита	cái lò
refrigerator (icebox)	refrigerador, nevera	réfrigérateur, glacière	frigorifero	Eisschrank	холодильник	tủ lạnh (ngăn đá)
bathtub	bañera, baño	baignoire	vasca da bagno	Badewanne	ванна	bồn tắm
toilet	excusado, retrete	cabinet, toilette	gabinetto	Toilette	уборная	phòng tắm
bookcase (shelves)	armario para libros (estantes)	bibliothèque (rayons)	libreria (scaffali)	Bücherschrank, Bücherregal	книжный шкаф (полки)	tủ đựng sách
picture	cuadro, pintura	image, tableau	quadri	Bilder	картины	hình ảnh
rug (carpet)	alfombra	tapis	tappeto	Teppich	ковёр	thảm
curtains	cortina(s)	rideau(x)	tendine	Gardinen	занавески	màn
waste (paper) basket	cesto	corbeille	cestino	Papierkorb	корзина для бумаги	giỏ đựng rác

Vocabulary Supplement
rooms of a house, Activities (11), Colors (1)

Grammar

Concepts: Demonstrative adjectives
Verbs: there is/are

Patterns

1. Point to the object and model the pattern for the students. Have them use it to identify the furnishings.
   This is a lamp. (couch, chair, table, etc.)
   Change the above to the plural.
   These are lamps. (couches, chairs, tables, etc.)
   Repeat, using **that** and **those.**
2. Complete the sentences with a logical answer.
   In the living room there is/are _____.
   (lamp, sofa, chair, table, curtains, rug, wastebasket, pictures, bookcase)
   In the dining room there is/are _____.
   (chair, table, curtains, rug, pictures)
   In the kitchen there is/are _____. (sink, stove, curtains, wastebasket, refrigerator)
   In the bathroom there is/are _____. (toilet, curtains, wastebasket, bathtub, rug)
   In the bedroom there is/are _____. (lamp,

   chair, table, dresser, curtains, bed, rug, wastebasket, pictures, bookcase)
   On the wall there is/are _____. (pictures)
3. Complete the sentences.
   I sit on a _____. (sofa, chair, bed)
   I cook on a _____. (stove)
   I put clothes in a _____. (dresser)
   I put books in a _____. (bookcase)
   I use a _____ to read at night. (lamp)
   I wash dishes in a _____. (sink)
   I put food in a _____. (refrigerator)
   I sleep on a _____. (bed)
   I wash myself in the _____. (bathtub)
   On the windows there are _____. (curtains)
   On the floor there is a _____. (rug)
   On the walls there are _____. (pictures)
   There are four chairs around the _____. (table)
   I put used paper in a _____. (wastebasket)

Activities

1. What is in the living room? (kitchen, bedroom, bathroom)
2. What color is the lamp? (sofa, chair, etc.)
3. What do you do with a stove? (couch, dresser, lamp, etc.)
4. Do you have a table? (dresser, stove, lamp, etc.)
5. Draw your living room and label the furnishings. (dining room, kitchen, bathroom, bedroom)
6. You are a piece of furniture about to be thrown out. What would you say to the owner to prove you still have a use?
7. Bingo: Read the sentences from Patterns, number 3 as the clues; the players cover up the answers.

18. Household Items

Vocabulary

English	Spanish	French	Italian	German	Russian	Vietnamese
tablecloth	mantel	nappe	tovaglia	Tischdecke	скáтерть	khăn trải bàn
napkin	servilleta	serviette	tovagliolo	Serviette	салфéтка	khăn ăn
frying pan	sartén	poêle	padella	Bratpfanne	сковорóдка	chảo
kettle	caldera, marmita	bouilloire, marmite	caldaia, pentola	Kessel	чáйник	ấm nước
towel	toalla	serviette	asciugamano	Handtuch	полотéнце	khăn mặt
radio	radio	radio	radio	Radio	рáдио	vô tuyến điện báo
clothes dryer	secadora, secador, máquina de secar	séchoir	asciugatrice	Wäschetrockner, Trockenmaschine	сушúлка	máy sấy quần aó
clothes washer	lavador, lavadora, máquina de lavar	machine à laver	lavatrice	Waschmaschine	стирáльная машúна	máy giặt quần aó
broom	escoba	balai	scopa	Besen	вéник	cái chổi
vacuum cleaner	aspiradora	aspirateur	aspirapolvere	Staubsauger	пылесóс	máy hút bụi
toaster	tostador	grille-pain	tostapane	Brotröster, Toaster	тóстер	máy nướng bánh mì
(electric) blender	licuadora	liquidateur	frullatore (elettrico)	Mixgerät, Mixer	(электрúческая) мешáлка	máy xay (điện)
(electric) fan	ventilador, abanico eléctrico	ventilateur	ventilatore	Ventilator	электрúческий вентилятор	quạt (điện)
television, television set	televisión, televisor	télévision, téléviseur	televisione, televisore	Fernsehapparat	телевúзор	vô tuyến truyền hình
pillow	almohada	oreiller	cuscino	Kissen	полýшка	gối
blanket	frazada, manta	couverture	coperta	Wolldecke	одеяло	chăn, mền

Vocabulary Supplement daily activities, rooms of a house, positions

Grammar

Concepts: Possessive adjectives
Verbs: Present tense

Patterns

1. Point to the object and model the pattern for the students. Have them use it to identify the household items.
    My mother has a frying pan. (kettle, towel, radio, etc.)
    Our mother has a frying pan. (kettle, towel, etc.)
    Your mother has a frying pan. (kettle, towel, etc.)
    His mother has a frying pan, etc.
    Their mother has a frying pan, etc.
    Change the above to the plural.

2. Complete the sentences with a logical answer.
    I wash clothes in a _____. (clothes washer)
    I put my head on a _____. (pillow)
    I dry myself with a _____. (towel)
    I clean the floor with a _____. (broom, vacuum cleaner)
    I cook eggs in a _____. (frying pan, kettle)
    I dry clothes in a _____. (clothes dryer)
    I put bread in a _____. (toaster)
    I watch movies on a _____. (television)

3. Complete the sentences with a logical answer.
    In the kitchen there is/are _____.
    In the bedroom there is/are _____.

Activities

1. Does your mother have a toaster?
    Does her sister have a broom?
    Does your house have a fan?
    Does my brother have a pillow?
    Does our aunt have a vacuum cleaner?

2. Change the above to the plural.
    Does your mother have toasters? or Do your mothers have toasters?

3. What do you do with a tablecloth? (kettle, vacuum cleaner)
    What do they do with a toaster? (broom, frying pan)
    What do I do with a radio? (towel, blender)
    What do we do with a pillow? (blanket, television)

4. Circle the things that are in a kitchen.
    Draw a line under the things that are in a bathroom.
    Draw an X through the things that are in a bedroom.

5. What is next to the tablecloth? (radio, television)
    What is on top of the blanket? (clothes washer, toaster)
    What is below the frying pan? (vacuum cleaner, blender)

6. Bingo: Read the sentences from Patterns, number 2 as the clues; the players cover up the answers.

19. Transportation

Vocabulary

English	Spanish	French	Italian	German	Russian	Vietnamese
airplane	aeroplano, avión	avion	aeroplano	Flugzeug	самолёт	tàu bay, máy bay
sailboat	barco de vela, velero	bateau à voiles	barca a vela	Segelschiff	парусная шлюпка	tàu buồm
bus	autobús, bus, guagua	autobus, bus	autobus	Omnibus	автобус	ô tô buýt
train	tren	train	treno	Zug	поезд	xe lửa, tàu hỏa
steamship (boat)	vapor	bateau à vapeur	piroscafo (nave)	Dampfer	пароход	tàu chạy bằng hơi nước
helicopter	helicóptero	hélicoptère	elicottero	Hubschrauber	геликоптёр	máy bay trực thăng
truck	camión	camion	camion	Lastwagen	грузовик	xe cam nhông
taxi, cab	taxi	taxi	tassì	Taxi	такси	xe tắc xi
balloon	aeróstato, globo aerostático	ballon	palloncino	Ballon	аэростат	bong bóng
car	automóvil, carro, coche	voiture, auto(mobile)	automobile	Auto	автомобиль	xe
bicycle	bicicleta	bicyclette, vélo	bicicletta	Fahrrad	велосипед	xe đạp
horse	caballo	cheval	cavallo	Pferd	лошадь	con ngựa
highway	carretera	grande route	autostrada	Landstraße	автострада, шоссейная дорога	xa lộ
motorcycle	motocicleta	moto(cyclette)	motocicletta	Motorrad	мотоцикл	xe máy dầu
canoe	canoa, chalupa	canoë	canoa	Kanu	челнок	thuyền nhỏ, ca nô
airport	aeropuerto	aéroport	aeroporto	Flughafen	аэропорт	phi trường

Vocabulary Supplement   vehicle parts

Grammar

Concepts: Subject/verb agreement, Present tense
Verbs: to be, to travel

Patterns

1. Point to the object and model the pattern for the students. Have them use it to identify the modes of transportation.

   I am on an airplane. (sailboat, steamship)
   They are in a helicopter. (airport, car, balloon)
   We are on a highway. (motorcycle, bus)
   You are on a train. (truck, bicycle)
   He is on a horse. (bus, canoe)

2. Complete the sentences with a logical answer.

   A (an) _____ flies in the sky. (airplane, helicopter)

   A _____ travels in water. (sailboat, steamship, canoe)

   Many cars travel on a _____ . (highway)

   Many planes are at an _____ . (airport)

   A _____ travels on a highway. (bus, truck, car, taxi, motorcyle)

   A _____ has wheels. (plane, car, motorcycle, bus, train, truck, taxi, bicycle)

   A _____ has no motor. (bicycle, horse, canoe, balloon, sailboat)

   A _____ has doors. (plane, steamship, helicopter, car, truck, train, bus, taxi)

3. Change the verb to agree with the new subject.

   I am on a bicycle. (we, you |pl.|, they, he, Mary, the boys)
   We travel by plane. (you |pl.|, they, he, Joe, the girls, I)

Activities

1. Answer the question in a complete sentence.
   What flies in the sky? (plane, helicopter, balloon)
   What has wheels? (truck, car, bus, etc.)
   What travels in water? (sailboat, steamship, canoe)
   What travels on a highway? (car, truck, bus, etc.)
   What has a motor? (plane, car, etc.)

2. Play "What am I?"
   Example: I have two wings.
   I fly in the sky.
   I fly very fast.
   What am I? (plane)

3. Bingo: Read the clues; the players cover up the answers.

car, another driver	(cab)
hot air, sky	(balloon)
wings, sky	(airplane)
wheels, legs	(bicycle)
four legs	(horse)
many planes	(airport)
motor, two wheels	(motorcycle)
motor, 2 or 4 doors	(car)
sky, no wings	(helicopter)
water, wind	(sailboat)
many cars	(highway)
many people, motor	(bus)
more than 4 wheels, big motor	(plane)
hot water, ocean	(steamship)
whistle, tracks	(train)
water, Indians	(canoe)

20. School

Vocabulary

English	Spanish	French	Italian	German	Russian	Vietnamese
classroom	sala de clase	salle de classe	aula	Klassenzimmer	класс	lớp học
teacher	maestro, maestra profesor, profesora	professeur	maestro (a)	Lehrer, Lehrerin	учитель	thầy giáo, cô giáo
student (pupil)	alumno, alumna	étudiant(e) (élève)	studente	Student (Schüler)	ученик, ученица	học sinh, học trò
book	libro	livre	libro	Buch	книга	sách
chalkboard	pizarra, pizarrón	tableau	lavagna	Tafel	доска	tấm bảng đen
chalk	gis, tiza	craie	gesso	Kreide	мел	phấn
eraser	borrador, goma	gomme, brosse	gomma	Radiergummi	тряпка, губка	cục tẩy
pen	pluma	stylo	penna	Kugelschreiber	(авто)ручка	cây viết mực
pencil	lápiz	crayon	matita	Bleistift	карандаш	cây viết chì
ruler	regla	règle	riga	Lineal	линейка	cái thước
paper	papel	papier	carta	Papier	бумага	giấy
desk	escritorio, pupitre	bureau, pupitre	banco, scrivania studentessa; alumno, -a	Schreibtisch	письменный стол, парта	bàn viết
map	mapa	carte	carta geografica	Landkarte	карта	tấm bản đồ
clock	reloj	horloge	orologio	Uhr	часы	đồng hồ treo tường
gymnasium	gimnasio	gymnase	palestra	Turnhalle	спортзал	phòng tập thể dục
playground	campo (parque) de recreo	cour de récréation	cortile	Spielplatz, Schulhof	спортплощадка	sân chơi

Vocabulary Supplement classroom activities, Colors (1)

Grammar

Concepts: Subject/verb agreement
Verbs: to see, to do

Patterns

1. Point to the object and model the pattern for the students. Have them use it to identify the objects.
   I see a teacher. (desk, ruler)
   We see a paper. (playground, book)
   She sees a chalkboard. (pencil, classroom)
   You see a student. (eraser, clock)
   They see a gymnasium. (map, pen)
   You (pl.) see chalk. (a teacher, student)
2. Complete the sentences with a logical answer.
   I write on paper with a ——— . (pencil)
   I write on a chalkboard with ——— . (chalk)
   I write on paper in ink with a ——— . (pen)
   I sit at a ——— . (desk)
   I read from a ——— . (book)

   I am a ——— . (student)
   I play on the ——— . (playground)
   I play basketball in the ——— . (gymnasium)
   I know the time from a ——— . (clock)
   I see different countries on a ——— . (map)
   I learn in a ——— . (classroom)
   I write on a ——— with chalk. (chalkboard)
   I use a ——— to make lines. (ruler)
3. Change the verb to agree with the new subject.
   I see the teacher. (we, you, he, they, you |pl.|, I, she, John)
   I see the book. (we, you, they, he, you |pl.|, I, she, Mary)

Activities

1. Ask the questions, changing the object.
   What do you see next to the paper? (ruler, desk)
   What do I see next to the pencil? (chalkboard, pencil)
   What do they see next to the clock? (eraser, student)
   What do we see next to the clock? (pen, map)
2. Ask the questions, changing the object.
   What do you do with a book? (desk, paper)
   What does a teacher do? (student)
   What does he do in the classroom? (gymnasium)
   What do they do with a chalkboard? (chalk, pencil)
   What do I do with a clock? (map, pen)
3. What is in your classroom?
   What color is it?
4. Answer the questions with a logical answer.
   On what do you sit? (desk)
   On what do you write? (paper, chalkboard)
   What do you read? (book, paper, map)
5. Bingo: Read the sentences from Patterns, number 2 as clues; the players cover up the answers. To win, the players should be able to give the object with the definite article, to use the plural form, to use the word correctly in a sentence, or whatever you deem appropriate.

21. Buildings

Vocabulary

English	Spanish	French	Italian	German	Russian	Vietnamese
house	casa	maison	casa	Haus	дом	nhà
apartment building	edificio de apartamentos (departamentos)	immeuble	palazzo	Wohnhaus	жилой дом	căn nhà lớn cho thuê
school	escuela, colegio	école, lycée	scuola	Schule	школа	trường học
library	biblioteca	bibliothèque	biblioteca	Bibliothek	библиотéка	thư viện
store	almacén, tienda	magasin, boutique	negozio	Geschäft, Laden	магазин	cửa tiệm
hospital	hospital	hôpital	ospedale	Krankenhaus	больница	bệnh viện
skyscraper	rascacielos	gratte-ciel	grattacielo	Wolkenkratzer	небоскрёб	nhà cao chọc trời
museum	museo	musée	museo	Museum	музéй	bảo tàng viện
church	iglesia	église	chiesa	Kirche	цéрковь	nhà thờ
factory	fábrica	usine	fabbrica	Fabrik	завóд	xưởng chế tạo
theater	teatro, cinema	théâtre, cinéma	teatro	Theater	теáтр	rạp hát, hý viện
grocery store (supermarket)	tienda de comestibles (supermercado)	épicerie (supermarché)	negozio alimentari (supermercato)	Lebensmittel-geschäft	гастронóм	tiệm bán thực phẩm (siêu thị)
gas station (service station)	estación de servicio	station-service	posto (stazione) di rifornimento	Tankstelle	стáнция обслýживания	
bank	banco	banque	banca	Bank	банк	ngân hàng
temple	templo, sinagoga	temple, synagogue	tempio	Tempel, Synagoge	храм	đền thờ
restaurant	restaurante	restaurant	ristorante	Restaurant	ресторáн	tiệm ăn, nhà hàng

Vocabulary Supplement daily activities

Grammar

Concepts: Subject/verb agreement
Verbs: to work, to live, to pray

Patterns

1. Point to the object and model the pattern for the students. Have them use it to identify the buildings.

   He works in a factory. (school, library, museum, store, theater, bank, grocery store, hospital, service station)
   I live in an apartment. (house, skyscraper)
   She prays in a church. (temple)

2. Complete the sentences with a logical answer.
   I buy food in a _____. (grocery store)
   I buy gas in a _____. (service station)
   I buy clothes in a _____. (clothing store)
   I save money in a _____. (bank)
   Doctors work in a _____. (hospital)
   We learn in a _____. (school)

   There are many books in a _____. (library)
   There are many paintings in a _____. (museum)
   I see movies in a _____. (theater)
   Many families live in an _____. (apartment building)
   We eat in a _____. (restaurant)
   One family lives in a _____. (house)
   A very tall building is a _____. (skyscraper)
   They make cars in a _____. (factory)
   We pray in a _____. (church, temple)

3. Change the verb to agree with the new subject.
   I work in a factory. (you, we, they, he, you |pl.|, she)
   I live in a house. (you, we, they, he, you |pl.|, she, John)
   I pray in a church. (you, we, they, you |pl.|, she, Mary)

Activities

1. Answer the questions with a logical response. What do you do in a school? (bank, library, hospital, etc.)

2. Answer the questions in a complete sentence.
   In what buildings do people live?
   In what buildings do people work?
   In what buildings do people pray?
   Do buildings have doors? (windows, a roof, walls, closets, floors)

3. Circle the buildings that you have been in. Draw an X through the buildings in which you can buy something.
   Draw a line under the buildings which can have an elevator.

4. Bingo: Read the clues from Patterns, number 2; the players cover up the answers.

5. Play "Who am I?"

6. You are a building about to be wrecked. Try to change the wrecker's mind.

22. Shops and Stores

Vocabulary

English	Spanish	French	Italian	German	Russian	Vietnamese
shoe store	zapatería	magasin de chaussures	negozio di scarpe	Schuhgeschäft	магазин обуви	tiệm bán giày
meat store (butcher shop)	carnicería	boucherie	macelleria	Metzgerei	мясной магазин	tiệm bán thịt
flower shop (florist)	tienda de flores	boutique de fleuriste	fiorista	Blumengeschäft	магазин цветов	tiệm bán bông
jewelry store	joyería	bijouterie	gioielleria	Juwelier	ювелирный магазин платья	tiệm bán châu báu
clothing store	tienda de ropa, ropería	magasin de vêtements	negozio di vestiti	Bekleidungsgeschäft	магазин готового	tiệm bán quần áo
drugstore	farmacia	pharmacie	farmacia	Drogerie	аптека	tiệm bán thuốc tây
fruit store	frutería	fruiterie	negozio di frutta	Obstladen	магазин фруктов	tiệm bán trái cây
pet shop	tienda de animales	magasin des animaux	negozio di animali domestici	Tierhandlung	зоологический магазин	tiệm bán gia súc
barbershop	barbería, peluquería	salon de coiffure	barberia	Friseur	мужская парикмахерская	tiệm cắt tóc
beauty salon	salón de belleza	salon de beauté	salone di bellezza	Friseur	женская парикмахерская	tiệm mỹ dung
camera store	tienda fotográfica	magasin d'appareils photographiques	negozio di macchine fotografiche	Photogeschäft, Photohändler	фотоотдел	tiệm bán máy ảnh
furniture store	mueblería	magasin d'ameublement	negozio di mobilia	Möbelgeschäft, Möbelhändler	магазин мебели	tiệm bán bàn ghế
car dealer	agencia de automóviles	concessionnaire de voitures	negoziante di automobili	Autohandlung	агент по продаже автомобилей	tiệm bán xe ô tô
bookstore	librería	librairie	libreria	Buchhandlung	книжный магазин	tiệm bán sách
bicycle shop	tienda de bicicletas	magasin de bicyclettes	negozio di biciclette	Fahrradhändler	магазин велосипедов	tiệm bán xe đạp
bakery	panadería	boulangerie	panetteria	Bäckerei	булочная	tiệm bán bánh mì

Vocabulary Supplement Clothing (2), Accessories (3), Food (5, 6), Furnishings (17)

Grammar

Concepts: Subject/verb agreement
Verbs: to go (to), to buy

Patterns

1. Point to the object and model the pattern for the students. Have them use it to identify the stores.

   I am going to the shoe store. (bakery, drugstore, etc.)

   They are going to the butcher shop. (bookstore, florist, etc.)

   I buy clothes in a ———. (clothing store)
   I buy furniture in a ———. (furniture store)
   I buy shoes in a ———. (shoe store)
   I buy a bicycle in a ———. (bicycle shop)
   I buy cake in a ———. (bakery)
   I buy meat in a ———. (butcher shop)
   I buy fruit in a ———. (fruit store)
   I buy a car at a ———. (car dealer)
   I buy animals in a ———. (pet shop)
   A man has his hair cut at a ———. (barber shop)
   A woman has her hair cut at a ———. (beauty salon)

2. Complete the sentences with a logical answer.

   I buy flowers in a ———. (florist, flower shop)
   I buy a necklace in a ———. (jewelry store)
   I buy books in a ———. (bookstore)
   I buy a camera in a ———. (camera store)
   I buy medicine in a ———. (drugstore)

3. Reverse the above sentences and vary the subject.

   At a butcher shop we buy ———. (meat)
   In a drugstore he buys ———. (medicine)

Activities

1. Ask the questions, varying the store.
   What do you buy in a shoe store? (jewelry store, florist)
   What do I buy in a bakery? (clothing store, fruit store)
   What do we buy in a pet shop? (bookstore, drugstore)
   What does he buy in a furniture store? (camera store, butcher shop)
   What do you (pl.) do at the barber shop? (beauty salon)

2. Ask the questions, varying the subject.
   Are you going to the bakery? (they, I, you [pl.], she, we, the boys)

3. Answer the questions with a logical response.
   In which stores do you buy food? (bakery, fruit store, butcher shop)
   In which stores do you buy clothing? (shoe store, clothing store)

   What do you buy in a bakery? (pie, cake, bread, cookies, etc.)
   What do you buy in a fruit store? (apples, oranges, bananas, etc.)
   What do you buy in a jewelry store? (rings, watches, necklaces, etc.)
   What do you buy in a pet shop? (cats, dogs, fish, mice, etc.)
   What do you buy in a clothing store? (shirts, pants, etc.)
   What do you buy in a furniture store? (sofas, chairs, etc.)
   What do you buy in a drugstore? (pills, medicine, etc.)

4. Play "Who am I?"
5. What is your favorite store? Why?
6. Bingo: Read the clues from Patterns, number 2; the players cover up the answers.

23. Occupations and Professions

Vocabulary

English	Spanish	French	Italian	German	Russian	Vietnamese
policeman	policía	agent de police	poliziotto	Polizist	полицейский	cảnh sát
fireman	bombero	pompier	pompiere	Feuerwehrmann	пожарник	lính cứu hỏa
plumber	plomero	plombier	idraulico	Klempner	водопроводчик	thợ chì, thợ ống nước
doctor	doctor, doctora; médico	médecin, docteur	dottore	Arzt	врач	bác sĩ
nurse	enfermera	infirmier, infirmière	infermiera	Krankenschwester	медсестра	nữ khán hộ, y tá
dentist	dentista	dentiste	dentista	Zahnarzt	зубной врач	nha sĩ
carpenter	carpintero	charpentier	falegname	Zimmermann	плотник	thợ mộc
truck driver	chofer	camionneur, conducteur	autista di camion	Lastwagenfahrer	водитель грузовика	tài xế xe vận tải
pilot	piloto	pilote	pilota	Pilot	лётчик	phi công
mechanic	mecánico	mécanicien	mecanico	Mechaniker	механик	thợ máy
secretary (typist)	secretaria, mecanógrafo, -a	secrétaire (dactylo)	segretaria (dattilografo)	Sekretär, Sekretärin	секретарь-машинистка	thư ký
artist	artista	artiste	artista	Künstler	художник	nghệ sĩ
seamstress	costurera	couturière	sarta	Näherin	портниха	thợ khâu vá
soldier	soldado	soldat	soldato	Soldat	солдат	quân nhân, lính
musician	músico	musicien, musicienne	musicista	Musiker	музыкант	nhạc sĩ
farmer	granjero	agriculteur, fermier	contadino	Bauer	фермер	nhà nông, chủ nông trại

Vocabulary Supplement Buildings (21)

Grammar

Concepts: Noun/adjective agreement
Verbs: to want (to)

Patterns

1. Point to the object and model the pattern for the students. Have them use it to identify the occupations.

   He wants to be a plumber. (Continue with all occupations.)
   She wants to be a plumber. (Continue with all occupations.)

2. Complete the sentences.

   A ——— plays music. (musician)
   A ——— cleans teeth. (dentist)
   A ——— fixes cars. (mechanic)
   A ——— directs traffic. (policeman)
   A ——— helps when we are sick. (doctor)
   A ——— grows food. (farmer)
   A ——— protects the country. (soldier)
   A ——— drives a truck. (truck driver)
   A ——— helps a doctor. (nurse)
   A ——— flies a plane. (pilot)
   A ——— builds houses. (carpenter)
   Continue with all the occupations.

3. Change the verb to agree with the new subject. He wants to be a mechanic. (I, they, she, you |pl.|, he, you)

Activities

1. Ask the questions, changing the subject.
   Do you want to be a pilot? (he, they, you |pl.|, I, she, Joe, Mary)

2. Answer the questions with a logical response.
   What does a policeman do? (Continue with all occupations.)

3. Complete the sentences, telling where each person works.
   A policeman works ——— . (in the city, on the street, in a car, etc.)
   A pilot works in a ——— . (plane)
   Continue with all the occupations.

4. If the students do not have the vocabulary necessary to answer the above questions, first ask the following questions.
   Does a policeman work in the city?
   Does a pilot work in a plane?, etc.

5. Circle the people who wear a uniform.
   Draw a line under the people who work in a [building?]

6. What color is the uniform of the doctor? (nurse, policeman, etc.)
   Draw an X through the people who do not work in a building.

7. Bingo: Read the clues from Patterns, number 2; the players cover up the answers.

8. Which occupation or profession do you want to see eliminated? Why?
   Play "Who am I?"

9. What do you want to be?

24. Domestic Animals

Vocabulary

English	Spanish	French	Italian	German	Russian	Vietnamese
cat	gato	chat	gatto	Katze	кот	con mèo
dog	perro	chien	cane	Hund	собáка	con chó
horse	caballo	cheval	cavallo	Pferd	лóшадь	con ngựa
bird	ave, pájaro	oiseau	uccello	Vogel	птйца	con chim
fish	pez	poisson	pesce	Fisch	рыба	con cá
cow	vaca	vache	vacca	Kuh	корóва	con bò cái
chicken	pollo, gallina	poule	gallina	Huhn	кýрица	con gà
pig	cerdo, lechón, puerco	cochon	maiale, porco	Schwein	свинья	con heo
goat	cabra, chivo	chèvre	capra	Ziege	козá	con dê
mouse	ratón	souris	sorcio, topo	Maus	мышь	con chuột
fly	mosca	mouche	mosca	Fliege	мýха	con ruôi
bee	abeja	abeille	ape	Biene	пчелá	con ong
snake	culebra, víbora, serpiente	serpent	serpe, serpente, biscia	Schlange	змея	con rắn
rabbit	conejo	lapin	coniglio	Kaninchen	крóлик	con thỏ
turtle	tortuga	tortue	tartaruga	Schildkröte	черепáха	con rùa
sheep	oveja, carnero	mouton	pecora	Schaf	овцá	con cừu

Vocabulary Supplement Colors (1)

Grammar

Concepts: Noun/adjective agreement
Verbs: to be (is/are)

Patterns

1. Point to the object and model the pattern for the students. Have them use it to identify the animals.

   This animal is a small fly. (fish, rabbit, turtle, snake, chicken, cat, bee, dog, mouse, bird, sheep)

   This animal is a large pig. (cow, goat, horse)

   Change the above to the plural.
   These animals are small flies, etc.
   These animals are large pigs, etc.

2. Complete the sentences with a logical answer.

   A _____ flies. (fly, bee, bird, chicken)
   A _____ lives in the water. (fish, turtle)
   A _____ is long and thin. (snake)
   A _____ lives on a farm. (pig, cow, goat, rabbit, horse, sheep, chicken)
   A _____ eats cheese. (mouse)
   A _____ says meow. (cat)

   A _____ says bowwow. (dog)

3. Complete the sentences with a correct color.
   A fly is _____ . (black)
   A pig is _____ . (gray)
   Continue with all the animals.

Activities

1. Answer the question in a complete sentence.
   Which animals are small? (large)
   What color is a fly? (pig, goat, etc.)

2. Answer the questions with a logical response.
   Which animals live in water? (fish, turtle)
   Which animals walk on two legs? (chicken, bird)
   Which animals walk on four legs? (pig, cow, goat, rabbit, turtle, horse, cat, dog, mouse, sheep)
   Which animals fly? (fly, bee, bird)
   Which animals do not have legs? (snake, fish)
   Which animals live on a farm? (goat, pig, cow, etc.)
   Which animals move quickly? (fly, rabbit, fish, etc.)
   Which animals move slowly? (turtle, snake, etc.)
   Which animals can you have in your home? (fly, fish, cat, etc.)
   Which animal would you like to be? Why?

3. Play "Who am I?"

4. Which animal do you like the most? (the least) Why?

5. Complete the sentence: If I were a fly (pig, cow, etc.), I would _____ .

Vocabulary

English	Spanish	French	Italian	German	Russian	Vietnamese
lion	león	lion	leone	Löwe	лев	con sư tử
bear	oso	ours	orso	Bär	медведь	con gấu
hippopotamus	hipopótamo	hippopotame	ippopotamo	Nilpferd	гиппопотам	con hà mã
alligator	caimán, lagarto	alligator	alligatore	Alligator	аллигáтор	con cá sấu
monkey	mono, mico	singe	scimmia	Affe	обезьяна	con khi
zebra	cebra	zèbre	zebra	Zebra	зебра	con ngựa vằn
rhinoceros	rinoceronte	rhinocéros	rinoceronte	Nashorn	носорóг	con tê giác
tiger	tigre	tigre	tigre	Tiger	тигр	con hổ
camel	camello	chameau	cammello	Kamel	верблюд	con lạc đà
elephant	elefante	éléphant	elefante	Elefant	слон	con voi
dinosaur	dinosauro	dinosaurien	dinosauro	Dinosaurier	динозáвр	con khủng long
giraffe	jirafa	girafe	giraffa	Giraffe	жирáф	con hươu cổ cao
deer	ciervo, venado	cerf	cervo	Reh	олéнь	con nai
whale	ballena	baleine	balena	Wal(fisch)	кит	con cá voi
eagle	águila	aigle	aquila	Adler	орёл	con phượng hoàng
shark	tiburón	requin	squalo	Haifisch	акýла	con cá mập

Vocabulary Supplement Colors (1), Parts of the Body (7)

Grammar

Concepts: Demonstrative adjectives, Noun/
  adjective agreement
Verbs: to be (is/are), to live

Patterns

1. Point to the object and model the pattern for
   the students. Have them use it to identify the
   animals.
   This animal is a lion. (bear, monkey, etc.)
   That animal is a zebra. (bear, lion, etc.)
   Change the above to the plural.
   These animals are lions. (bears, tigers, etc.)
   Those animals are zebras. (bears, lions, etc.)
2. Complete the sentences with a logical answer.
   An _____ flies. (eagle)
   A _____ lives in water. (whale, shark)
   A _____ lives in water and on land.
   (hippopotamus, rhinoceros, alligator)
   A _____ lives on land. (lion, bear, monkey,
   zebra, camel, elephant, deer, tiger,
   dinosaur, giraffe)
   A _____ likes to climb trees. (monkey)
   A _____ has a long neck. (giraffe)
   An _____ has very large ears. (elephant)
3. Complete the answers with the correct colors.

   A lion is _____. (brown, yellow)
   An alligator is _____. (brown, green)
   Continue with all the animals.

Activities

1. Answer the questions in a complete sentence.
   Which animals are small? (large)
   What color is a lion? (bear, whale, etc.)
2. Answer the questions with a logical response.
   Where does a lion live? (bear, monkey, etc.)
   Which animal flies? (eagle)
   Which animals live on land? (lion, bear, etc.)
   Which animals live in water and on land?
   (alligator, etc.)
   Continue with all the animals.
3. Bingo: Read the following clues; the players
   cover up the answers.
   I lived a long time ago and only my bones
     are around today. (dinosaur)
   I have a very long neck. (giraffe)
   I live in the water and I have very sharp
     teeth. (shark)
   I like to sit in trees and I eat bananas.
     (monkey)
   I live in the desert and some people ride me.
     (camel)
   I pull Santa Claus' sleigh. (reindeer)
   I look like a horse with stripes. (zebra)
   I live in water and on land and I have sharp
     teeth. (alligator)
   I live in the jungle and I am the king. (lion)
   I can swim and I have a horn on my head.
     (rhino)
   I look like a large cat with stripes. (tiger)
   I fly in the sky. (eagle)
   I have very big ears and I like to eat
     peanuts. (elephant)
   I live on land and I sleep all winter. (bear)
   I live in water and I can shoot water from
     my head. (whale)
   I am very large and I live on land or in
     water. (hippo)
4. What is your favorite animal? Why?
5. Which animal would you like to be? Why?
6. Play "Who am I?"
7. Play "If I were a _____, I would _____."

26. Nature

Vocabulary

English	Spanish	French	Italian	German	Russian	Vietnamese
ocean	océano	océan	oceano	Ozean	океа́н	đại dương
river	río	fleuve, rivière	fiume	Fluß	река́	sông
mountain	montaña	montagne	montagna	Berg	гора́	núi
tree	árbol	arbre	albero	Baum	де́рево	cây
leaf	hoja	feuille	foglia	Blatt	лист	lá cây
branch	rama	branche, rameau	ramo	Ast	ветвь	cành cây, nhánh cây
grass	césped, hierba, pasto	herbe	erba	Gras	трава́	cỏ
plant	planta	plante	pianta	Pflanze	расте́ние	cây nhỏ, thảo mộc
flower	flor	fleur	fiore	Blume	цвето́к	bông hoa
sky	cielo	ciel	cielo	Himmel	не́бо	bầu trời
valley	valle	vallée	valle	Tal	доли́на	thung lũng
lake	lago	lac	lago	See	о́зеро	cái hồ
beach	playa	plage	spiaggia	Strand	пляж	bờ biển
desert	desierto	désert	deserto	Wüste	пусты́ня	sa mạc
forest	bosque, selva	forêt	bosco	Wald	лес	rừng
bush	arbusto, mata	buisson	cespuglio	Busch	куст	bụi rậm

Vocabulary Supplement descriptive adjectives, Colors (1)

Grammar

Concepts: Demonstrative adjectives, Noun/
adjective agreement
Verbs: to go

Patterns

1. Point to the object and model the pattern for
the students. Have them use it to identify the
objects.
   This is a river. (mountain, tree, plant, etc.)
   That is a river. (mountain, tree, etc.)
   Change the above to the plural.
   These are rivers. (mountains, trees, etc.)
   Those are rivers. (mountains, trees, etc.)
2. Complete the sentences with a logical answer.
   I swim in an _____. (ocean, river, lake, at
   the beach)
   A _____ grows. (tree, plant, branch, grass,
   leaf, bush, flower, forest)
   Planes fly in the _____. (sky)
   A _____ is very hot and dry. (desert)
3. Complete the sentence with an appropriate
adjective.
   The ocean is _____.
   The river is _____.
   Continue with all the objects.

Activities

1. Answer the questions in a complete sentence.
   Where can you swim? (ocean, river, beach,
   lake)
   What can you climb? (mountain, tree,
   branch)
   What grows on a tree? (branch, leaf)
   What grows on the ground? (tree, grass,
   bush, flower, plant)
   What is hot and dry? (desert)
   Where do many trees grow? (forest)
2. Answer in complete sentences.
   Are you going to swim in the ocean?
   Is she going to swim in the river?
   Are they going to swim in the lake?
   Are we going to swim at the beach?
   Are you going to climb the tree?
   Am I going to climb the mountain?
   Are they going to walk through the forest?
   Is he going to walk through the grass?
3. Complete the sentences with the correct
colors.
   The ocean is _____. (blue, green)
   The river is _____. (blue, green)
   Continue with all the objects.
4. Circle the things that grow.
5. Answer in a complete sentence.
6. Is there an ocean where you live? (grass,
   desert, forest, valley, sky, river)
   Are there mountains? (rivers, bushes,
   beaches, trees, plants)
   What animals live in the ocean? (river,
   mountains, trees, grass, desert, lakes,
   forests, sky)

Vocabulary

English	Spanish	French	Italian	German	Russian	Vietnamese
summer	verano	été	estate	Sommer	лéто	mùa hè
fall	otoño	automne	autunno	Herbst	óсень	mùa thu
winter	invierno	hiver	inverno	Winter	зимá	mùa đông
spring	primavera	printemps	primavera	Frühjahr	веснá	mùa xuân
rain	lluvia	pluie	pioggia	Regen	дождь	mưa
snow	nieve	neige	neve	Schnee	снег	tuyết
wind	viento	vent	vento	Wind	вéтер	gió
sun	sol	soleil	sole	Sonne	сóлнце	mặt trời
cloud	nube	nuage	nuvola	Wolke	óблако	mây
star	estrella	étoile	stella	Stern	звездá	sao
moon	luna	lune	luna	Mond	лунá	mặt trăng
lightning	relámpago	éclair	fulmine, lampo	Blitz	мóлния	chớp, sét
to be hot	hacer calor	faire chaud	fare caldo	heiß sein	комý-л. жáрко	nóng
to be cold	hacer frío	faire froid	fare freddo	frieren	комý-л. хóлодно	lạnh
ice	hielo	glace	ghiaccio	Eis	лёд	nước đá
storm	tempestad, temporal	orage, tempête	temporale, burrasca	Sturm	бýря	bão tố

Vocabulary Supplement Activities (11)

Grammar

Concepts: None
Verbs: weather expressions, to see

Patterns

1. Point to the object and model the pattern for the students. Have them use it to identify the objects.

   It is summer. (fall, winter, spring)
   There is a cloud. (rain, moon, storm, lightning, star, etc.)
   I am cold. (hot)

2. Complete the sentences with a logical response.

   In the summer it is _____. (hot, rainy, etc.)
   In the winter it is _____. (cold, snowy)
   During a storm there is _____. (rain, lightning)
   The trees move when it is _____. (windy, stormy)
   I see the _____ at night. (stars, moon)

3. Change the sentence to agree with the new subject.

   I see the moon. (you, we, he, you [pl.], Mary, she, I)

Activities

1. Answer the questions with a logical response.
   When is it hot? (cool, cold)
   When do leaves grow on trees?
   What do you do when it is cloudy? (raining, sunny, windy, lightning, snowing, cold, hot, winter, summer)
   Do you have snow where you live? (storms)
   When do you see the moon? (sun, stars, clouds, lightning, ice, snow, leaves falling, leaves growing)
2. What is your favorite season? Why?
3. Play "Who am I?"

28. Tools and Materials

Vocabulary

English	Spanish	French	Italian	German	Russian	Vietnamese
saw	sierra, serrucho	scie	sega	Säge	пила́	cái cưa
rake	rastro, rastrillador	râteau	rastrello	Rechen, Harke	гра́бли	cái cào
screwdriver	destornillador	tournevis	cacciavite	Schraubenzieher	отвёртка	cái vặn vít
pliers	alicates	pinces	pinze	Zange	щипцы́	cây kìm
nail	clavo	clou	chiodo	Nagel	гвоздь	cây đinh
shovel	pala	pelle	pala	Schaufel	лопа́та	cái xẻng
axe	hacha	hache	accetta	Axt	топо́р	cái rìu
hammer	martillo	marteau	martello	Hammer	молото́к	cái búa
wood	madera	bois	legno	Holz	де́рево	gỗ, mộc
glass	vidrio	verre	vetro	Glas	стекло́	kiến, gương, pha lê
plastic	plástico	plastique	plastico	Plastik, Kunststoff	пластма́сса	nhựa
rubber	caucho, goma	caoutchouc	gomma	Gummi	каучу́к, рези́на	cao su
metal	metal	métal	metallo	Metall	мета́лл	kim khí
cement	cemento	ciment	cemento	Zement	цеме́нт	xi măng
brick	ladrillo	brique	mattone	Backstein	кирпи́ч	gạch
scissors	tijeras	ciseaux	forbici	Schere	но́жницы	cái kéo

Vocabulary Supplement none

Grammar

Concepts: Demonstrative adjectives
Verbs: to be (is/are), to use

Patterns

1. Point to the object and model the pattern for the students. Have them use it to identify the tools and materials.
   This is a saw. (rake, screwdriver, wood, glass, etc.)
   There are scissors. (pliers)
   Change the above to **that** and **those.**
   That is a saw, etc.
   Those are scissors, etc.
2. Model the pattern for the students.
   This is made of wood. (glass, rubber, etc.)
   That is made of wood. (glass, rubber, etc.)
3. Complete the sentences with a logical answer.
   A bottle is made of _____. (glass)
   A carpenter cuts wood with a _____. (saw)
   Streets are made of _____. (cement)
   A ball is made of _____. (rubber)
   To cut down a tree I use an _____. (axe)
   I use a _____ to pick up leaves. (rake)
   I cut paper with a _____. (scissors)
   A tree gives us _____. (wood)
   A car is made of _____. (metal)

I make a hole in the ground with a _____. (shovel)
I tighten a screw with a _____. (screwdriver)
I put in a _____ with a hammer. (nail)
Many houses are made of _____. (brick)
Many toys are made of _____. (plastic)
I use a _____ to put in a nail. (hammer)
A plumber uses _____ on pipes. (pliers)

Activities

1. Point to the object and ask the questions:
   What is this? (that)
   What is it made of?
2. Complete the sentences with a logical answer.
   A _____ is made of glass. (wood, plastic, metal, rubber, etc.)
   A carpenter uses a _____. (screwdriver, hammer, nail, etc.)
   A plumber uses a _____. (pliers, screwdriver, etc.)
3. Bingo: Read the sentences from Patterns, number 3 as clues; the players cover up the answers.
4. Play "What am I?"

29. Communication

Vocabulary

English	Spanish	French	Italian	German	Russian	Vietnamese
letter	carta	lettre	lettera	Brief	письмо́	thư, bức thư
newspaper	periódico	journal	giornale	Zeitung	газе́та	nhật báo
satellite	satélite	satellite	satellite	Satellit	спу́тник	vệ tinh
telephone	teléfono	téléphone	telefono	Telephon	телефо́н	máy điện thoại
radio	radio	radio	radio	Radio	ра́дио	vô tuyến truyền thanh
record	disco	disque	disco	Schallplatte	пласти́нка	thu lại, đĩa hát
magazine	revista	revue	rivista	Magazin	журна́л	tạp chí
mouth	boca	bouche	bocca	Mund	рот	miệng
television	televisión	télévision	televisione, televisore	Fernsehapparat	телеви́зор	vô tuyến truyền hình
telegram	telegrama	télégramme	telegramma	Telegramm	телегра́мма	điện tín
poster/billboard	cartel	affiche, tableau d'affichage	cartellone/pannello	Plakat	доска́ объявле́ний	giấy yết thị
C.B. radio	radio C.B.	radio C.B.	radio (cittadino)	Funktelephon	коротковолно́вый приёмник	máy truyền tin
gestures	gestos	gestes	gesti	Gebärde	ми́мика	điệu bộ
traffic signal	luz de tránsito, semáforo	feu	semaforo	Verkehrssignal	светофо́р	dấu hiệu giao thông
movies	cine, películas	cinéma, films	cinema	Kino, Filme	кино́	xi nê, chiếu bóng
book	libro	livre	libro	Buch	кни́га	cuốn sách

Vocabulary Supplement Parts of the Body (7)

Grammar

Concepts: Demonstrative adjectives
Verbs: to read, to listen

Patterns

1. Point to the object and model the pattern for the students. Have them use it to identify the objects.
   This is a letter. (newspaper, satellite, etc.)
   That is a letter. (newspaper, book, etc.)
2. Complete the sentences with a logical answer.
   I read a _____ . (newspaper, magazine, book, telegram, poster)
   My friend sends me a _____ . (letter)
   I listen to a _____ . (record, radio, C.B. radio)
   I talk to my friend with my _____ . (mouth, telephone)
   I watch programs on _____ . (television)

There is a _____ in the sky. (satellite)
A _____ tells cars to stop and to go. (traffic signal)
John Wayne and Paul Newman are in the _____ . (movies)

3. Change the sentence to agree with the new subject.
   I read a book. (we, you, the boys, she, you |pl.|, they)
   He listens to the radio. (we, you, the girls, she, you |pl.|, they)

Activities

1. Answer the questions in a complete sentence.
   Do you read a book? (they, he, we, I, she, you |pl.|)
   Do we listen to the radio? (they, he, you, I, she, you |pl.|)
   What do you read?
   To what do you listen?
   For what do you use your mouth? (ears, hands)
   Do you receive letters?
   Do you go to the movies?
   What do you watch on television?
   Do you listen to the radio?
   Do you have any records? (a television, a C.B. radio, a telephone)
2. Circle the objects you read.
   Draw an X through the objects you listen to.
3. Bingo: Read the clues from Patterns, number 2; the players cover up the answers.
4. Play "What am I?"

30. The Calendar

Vocabulary

English	Spanish	French	Italian	German	Russian	Vietnamese
Sunday	domingo	dimanche	domenica	Sonntag	воскресéнье	chúa nhựt
Monday	lunes	lundi	lunedì	Montag	понедéльник	thứ hai
Tuesday	martes	mardi	martedì	Dienstag	втóрник	thứ ba
Wednesday	miércoles	mercredi	mercoledì	Mittwoch	средá	thứ tư
Thursday	jueves	jeudi	giovedì	Donnerstag	четвéрг	thứ năm
Friday	viernes	vendredi	venerdì	Freitag	пя́тница	thứ sáu
Saturday	sábado	samedi	sabato	Samstag, Sonnabend	суббóта	thứ bảy
day	día	jour, journée	giorno	Tag	день	ngày
week	semana	semaine	settimana	Woche	недéля	tuần
month	mes	mois	mese	Monat	мéсяц	tháng
year	año	an, année	anno	Jahr	год	năm
date	fecha	date	data	Datum	числó	ngày, tháng
January	enero	janvier	gennaio	Januar	янвáрь	tháng một, tháng giêng
February	febrero	février	febbraio	Februar	феврáль	tháng hai
March	marzo	mars	marzo	März	март	tháng ba
April	abril	avril	aprile	April	апрéль	tháng tư
May	mayo	mai	maggio	Mai	май	tháng năm
June	junio	juin	giugno	Juni	июнь	tháng sáu
July	julio	juillet	luglio	Juli	июль	tháng bảy
August	agosto	août	agosto	August	áвгуст	tháng tám
September	septiembre	septembre	settembre	September	сентя́брь	tháng chín
October	octubre	octobre	ottobre	Oktober	октя́брь	tháng mười
November	noviembre	novembre	novembre	November	ноя́брь	tháng mười một
December	diciembre	décembre	dicembre	Dezember	декáбрь	tháng mười hai

Vocabulary Supplement Activities (11), today, yesterday, tomorrow, next, last

Grammar

Concepts: Past tense
Verbs: to be (is/was)

Patterns

1. Point to the day on the calendar and model the sentence for the students. Have them use it to identify the days of the week and the months of the year.

Today is Sunday. (Monday, Tuesday, etc.)
Tomorrow is Monday. (Tuesday, Wednesday, etc.)
Yesterday was Tuesday. (Monday, Sunday, etc.)

This month is January. (February, March, etc.)
Last month was December. (January, February, etc.)
Next month is February. (March, April, etc.)

2. Complete the sentences with a logical answer.
Today is _____.
Tomorrow is _____.
Yesterday was _____.
Today is Monday. (Tuesday, Wednesday, etc.) Tomorrow is _____.
Yesterday was Monday. (Tuesday. Sunday, etc.) Today is _____.
This month is January. (February, March, etc.) Next month is _____.
Last month was December. (January, March, etc.) This month is _____.

Activities

1. Give the days of the week backwards.
   Give the months of the year backwards.
2. Answer the questions in a complete sentence.
   What day is it?
   What day was yesterday?
   What day is tomorrow?
   What month is it?
   What is next month?
   What was last month?
   In what month is your birthday?
   What year is it?
   What was last year?
   What is next year?
   How many days are in a week?
   How many weeks are in a month?
   How many months are in a year?
   What days do you go to school?
   What days do you not go to school?
   In what months do you go to school?
   In what months do you not go to school?
   In what months is it cold? (hot)
   In what months do you ice skate? (ski, swim, play baseball)
   What is the date? (tomorrow's date, yesterday's date)
   What is your favorite day (month)? Why?

31. Holidays and Celebrations

Vocabulary

English	Spanish	French	Italian	German	Russian	Vietnamese
Christmas	Navidad	Noël	Natale	Weihnachten	Рождество́	lễ chúa giáng sinh
Thanksgiving	Día de dar gracias	Jour de grâces, Thanksgiving	giorno di ringraziamento	Erntedankfest	День благо-да́рности	lễ tạ ơn
New Year's	Día del año nuevo	Jour de l'An	Capo d'anno	Neujahr	Но́вый год	tết, năm mới
Independence Day	Día de la independencia	quatre juillet, jour de l'indépendance	giorno della libertà	Unabhängigkeitstag	День незави́симости	lễ độc lập
birthday	cumpleaños	anniversaire	compleanno	Geburtstag	день рожде́ния	lễ sinh nhật
Halloween	—	Veille de la Toussaint	vigilia di tutti i santi	Abend vor Allerheiligen	Халлоуи́н	đêm hiển linh
Valentine's Day	Día de San Valentín, Día de los enamorados	la Saint-Valentin	giorno di San Valentino (degli innamorati)	Valentinstag	День св. Валенти́на	ngày tình thương
Mother's Day	Día de las madres	Fête des mères	giorno della mamma	Muttertag	День матере́й	ngày nhớ nghĩa mẹ
Father's Day	Día de los padres	Fête des pères	giorno del papà	Vatertag	День отцо́в	ngày nhớ ơn cha
Armed Forces Day	Día de la fuerzas armadas	—	giorno dei militari	Tag der Wehrmacht	День вооружённых си́лов	ngày quân lực
Labor Day	Día del trabajo	Fête du travail	giorno del lavoratore	Tag der Arbeit	День труда́	lễ lao động
St. Patrick's Day	Fiesta de San Patricio	la Saint-Patrick	giorno di San Patrizio	Patrickstag	День св. Патри́ка	lễ thánh Patrick
picnic	merienda campestre	pique-nique	scampagnata	Picknick	пикни́к	ăn ngoài trời
party	fiesta	fête, surprise-partie	festa	Fest, Party	ве́чер, вечери́нка	bữa tiệc
wedding	boda	noces	nozze	Hochzeit	сва́дьба	đám cưới
dance	baile, danza	bal, danse	ballo	Tanz	ве́чер та́нцев	khiêu vũ

Vocabulary Supplement   The Calendar (30)

Grammar

Concepts: Possessive adjectives
Verbs: to celebrate, to be

Patterns

1. Point to the day or celebration and model the pattern for the students. Have them use it to identify the holidays and celebrations.
   Today is Christmas. (New Year's, etc.)
   We are at a picnic. (party, dance, wedding)

2. Complete the sentences with a logical answer.
   I have a cake with candles on my ———.
   (birthday)
   I eat turkey on ———. (Thanksgiving)
   I see a bride at a ———. (wedding)
   I hear a band or records at a ———.
   (dance)

   I give presents to my mother on ———.
   (Mother's Day)
   We celebrate our country's birthday on
   ———. (Independence Day)
   We honor the workers on ———. (Labor
   Day)
   We honor the Irish on ———. (St. Patrick's
   Day)
   I talk to and dance with my friends at a
   ———. (party)
   I give presents to my father on ———.
   (Father's Day)
   We decorate a tree for ———. (Christmas)
   At midnight on December 31 we celebrate
   ———. (New Year's)
   I go trick or treating on ———.
   (Halloween)

   We honor the soldiers on ———. (Armed
   Forces Day)
   I remember the people I love on ———.
   (Valentine's Day)

3. Change the sentence to agree with the new subject.
   We are at a picnic. (you, I, she, they, you
   |pl.|, the girls)
   You celebrate your birthday. (I, we, they,
   she, you |pl.|, he)

Activities

1. How do you celebrate Christmas? (New Year's, etc.)
2. In what month is Christmas? (New Year's, etc.)
3. Do you go on picnics? (to parties, weddings, dances)
4. What is your favorite holiday? Why?
5. When is Christmas? (New Year's, Halloween, St. Patrick's Day, Valentine's Day, Independence Day)
6. Bingo: Read the clues from Patterns, number 2; the players cover up the answers.

32. The Map

Vocabulary

English	Spanish	French	Italian	German	Russian	Vietnamese
Africa	África	Afrique	Africa	Afrika	Áфрика	phi châu
Europe	Europa	Europe	Europa	Europa	Европа	âu châu
Asia	Asia	Asie	Asia	Asien	Áзия	á châu
North America	América del Norte	Amérique du Nord	Nordamerica	Nordamerika	Сéверная Амéрика	bắc mỹ
South America	América del Sur	Amérique du Sud	Sudamerica	Südamerika	Ю́жная Амéрика	nam mỹ
Australia	Australia	Australie	Australia	Australien	Австрáлия	úc châu
Antarctica	Antártica	Antarctique	Antartico	Antarktis	Антарктида	vùng nam' cực
north	norte	nord	nord	Norden	сéвер	hướng bắc
south	sur	sud	sud	Süden	юг	hướng nam
east	este	est	est	Osten	востóк	hướng đông
west	oeste	ouest	ovest	Westen	зáпад	hướng tây
country/nation	país/nación	pays/nation	paese/nazione	Land/Nation	странá	quốc gia

Vocabulary Supplement countries, nationalities

Grammar

Concepts: Noun/adjective agreement
Verbs: to live

Patterns

1. Point to the object and model the pattern for the students. Have them use it to identify the continents and directions.
   This is Africa. (Asia, Europe, etc.)
   That is Africa. (Asia, Europe, etc.)
2. Change the sentence to agree with the new subject.
   I live on the continent of North America.
   (we, the boys, she, they, you, he, you [pl.])
   I am an American. (she, we, they, you, the girls, you [pl.])
3. Give the continent for the following countries:
   Mexico is on the continent of _____.
   (Bolivia, Egypt, Switzerland, Rhodesia, Spain, China, Israel, Russia, Canada, Germany, New Zealand, Italy, the South Pole, France, England, the United States)

Activities

1. On what continent do you live? (the Soviets, Germans, French, Spanish, Mexicans, Swiss, Egyptians, Chinese, Australians)
2. Are you an American?
   Is she German?
   Are they French? etc.
3. Play "Where am I?"
4. On what continent would you like to live? Why?

NTC ESL/EFL TEXTS AND MATERIAL

Duplicating Masters and Blackline Masters

Easy Vocabulary Games
Vocabulary Games
Advanced Vocabulary Games
Beginning Activities for English
  Language Learners
Intermediate Activities for English
  Language Learners
Advanced Activities for English
  Language Learners
Play and Practice!
Basic Vocabulary Builder
Practical Vocabulary Builder

Computer Software

Amigo
Basic Vocabulary Builder
  on Computer

Dictionaries and References

English Picture Dictionary
Everyday American English Dictionary
Building Dictionary Skills in English
  (workbook)
Beginner's Dictionary of American
  English Usage
Beginner's English Dictionary
  Workbook
Dictionary of American Idioms
American English Idioms
Idiom Workbook
Essentials of English Grammar

Language and Culture Readers

Passport to America series
California Discovery
Adventures in the Southwest
The Coast-to-Coast Mystery
The New York Connection
Discover America series (text/audio-
  cassette)
New York
Chicago
California
Florida
Washington, D.C.
New England
Hawaii
Looking at American Signs
Looking at American Food
Looking at American Recreation
Looking at American Holidays

Teacher Resources

TESOL Professional Anthology series
Grammar and Composition
Listening, Speaking, and Reading
Culture
Teaching Culture
Speak with a Purpose!
Ideabook

For further information or a current catalog, write:
National Textbook Company
4255 West Touhy Avenue
Lincolnwood, Illinois 60646-1975 U.S.A.

1. Colors

Name_____
Date_____
Teacher_____

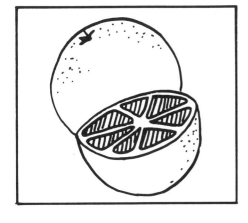

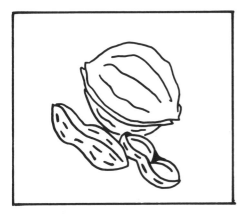

2. Clothing

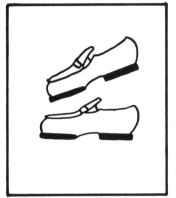

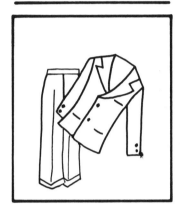

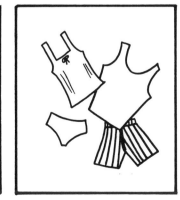

3. Accessories

 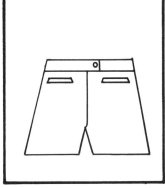 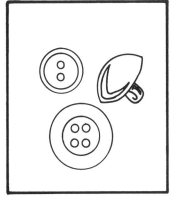 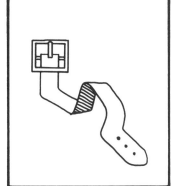

 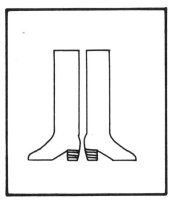 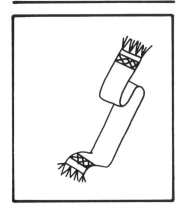 

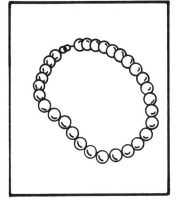 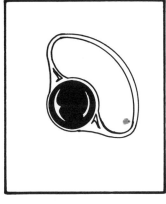 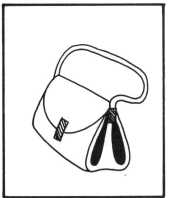 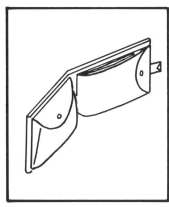

  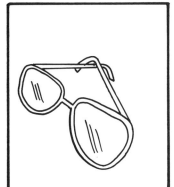 

4. Fruits and Vegetables

Name _____
Date _____
Teacher _____

 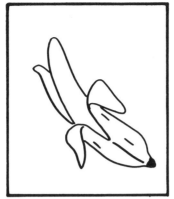  

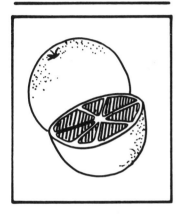   

   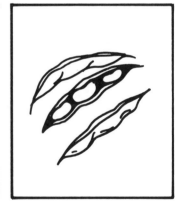

 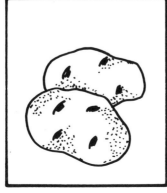  

5. Food—A

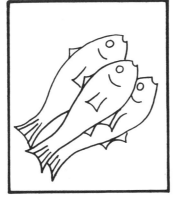

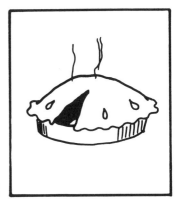

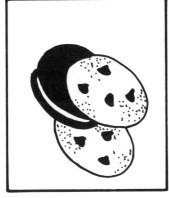
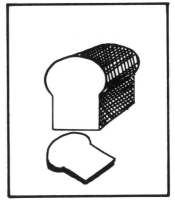
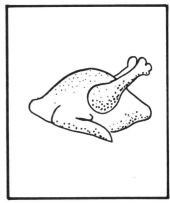

6. Food—B

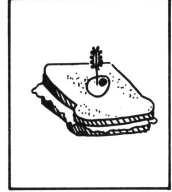

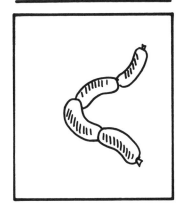

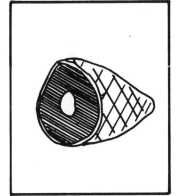

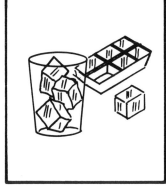
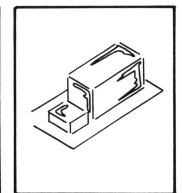

7. Parts of the Body

Name _____

Date _____

Teacher _____

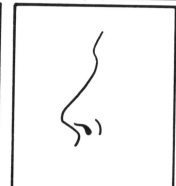

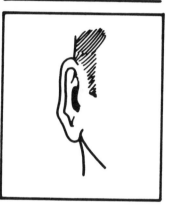
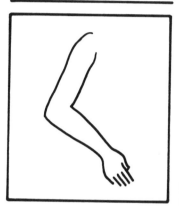

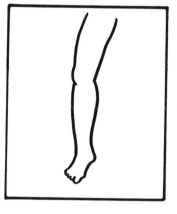
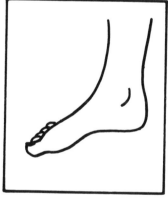
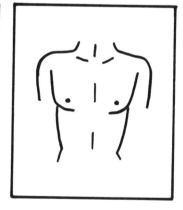
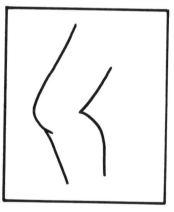

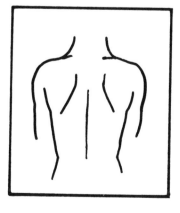

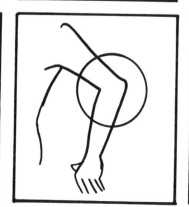
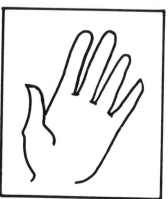

8. The Family

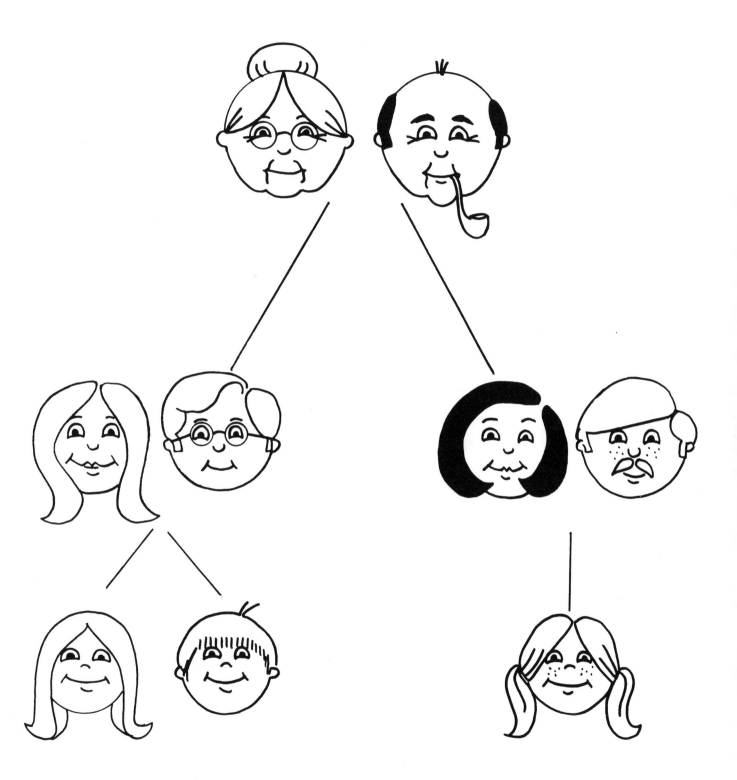

9. Miscellaneous

Name _____

Date _____

Teacher _____

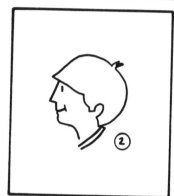

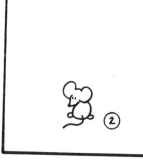

10. Health

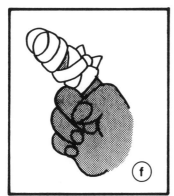

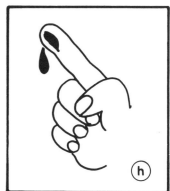

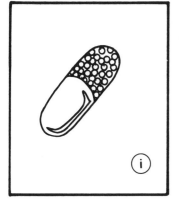

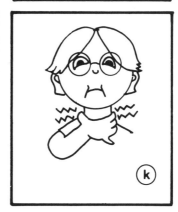

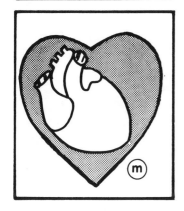

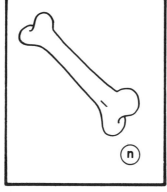

11. Activities

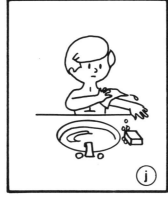

12. Sports and Recreation

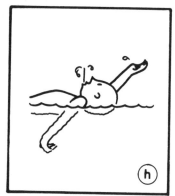

13. Numbers

Name _____
Date _____
Teacher _____

1	2	3	4
5	6	7	8
9	10	15	23
400	6000	1984	8,000,000

14. Telling Time

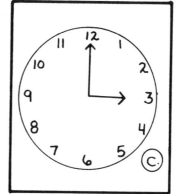

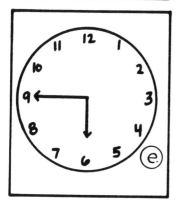

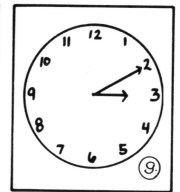
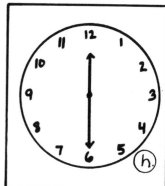

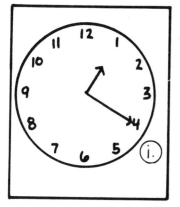

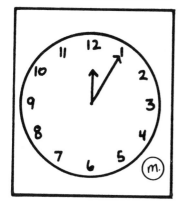
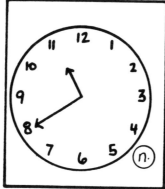

© National Textbook Company

15. Shapes and Containers

16. The House

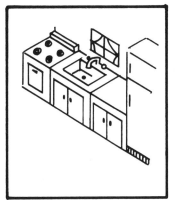
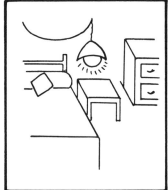

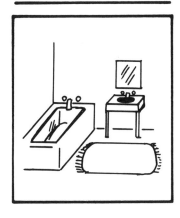

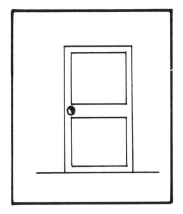

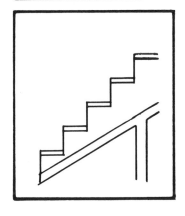
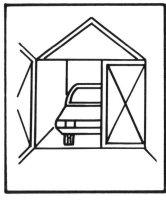

17. Furnishings

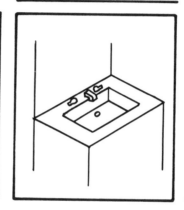

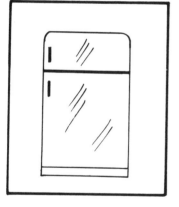
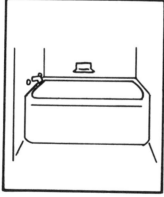

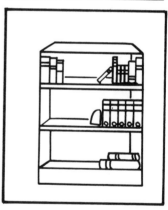

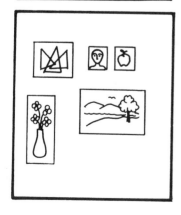
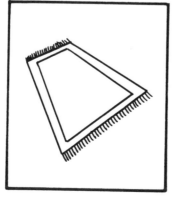
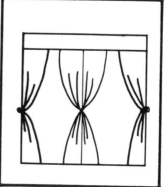

18. Household Items

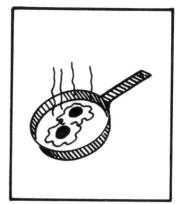

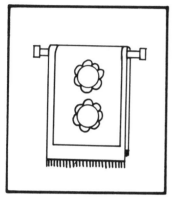
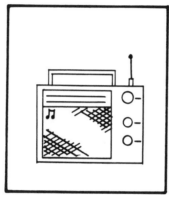

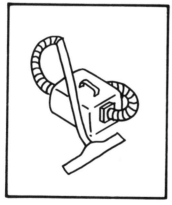

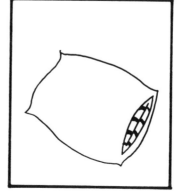
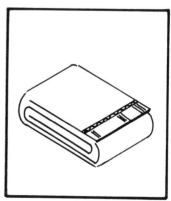

19. Transportation

  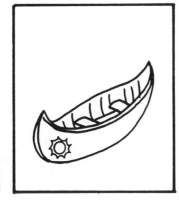 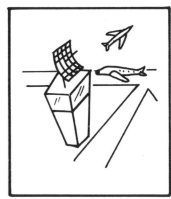

20. School

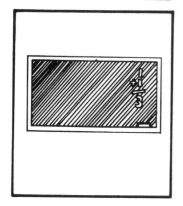

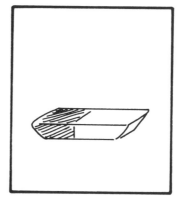

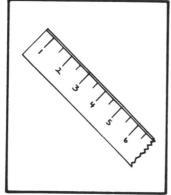
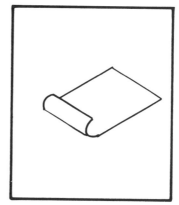

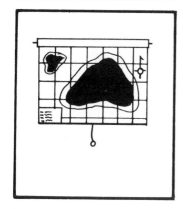

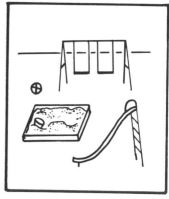

21. Buildings

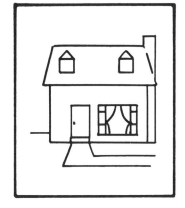

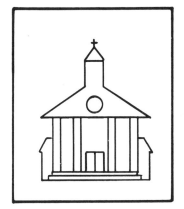

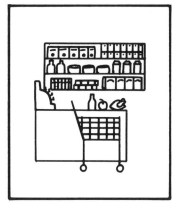

22. Shops and Stores

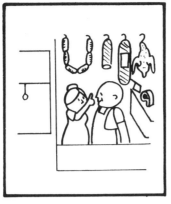

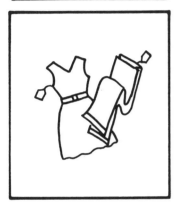

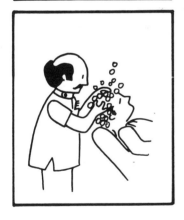

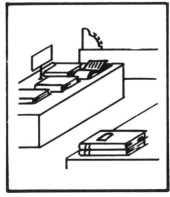

23. Occupations and Professions

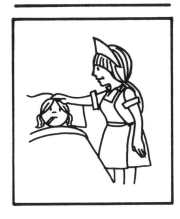

24. Domestic Animals

Name_____
Date_____
Teacher_____

 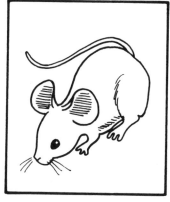  

25. Animals—B

Name_____
Date_____
Teacher_____

26. Nature

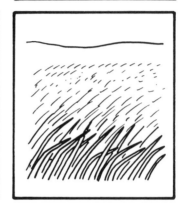

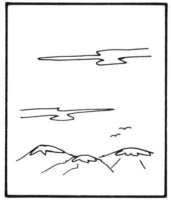

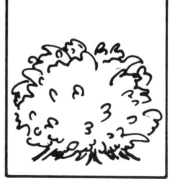

27. Seasons and Weather

Name _____
Date _____
Teacher _____

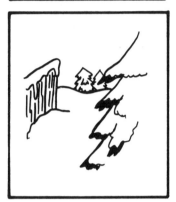

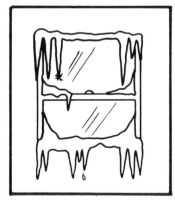

28. Tools and Materials

Name _____

Date _____

Teacher _____

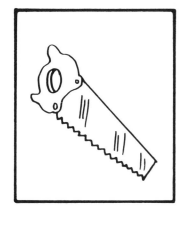

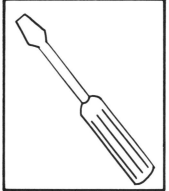
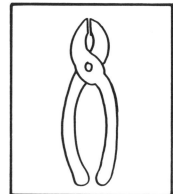

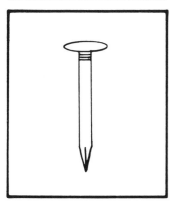

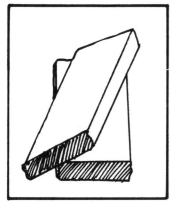

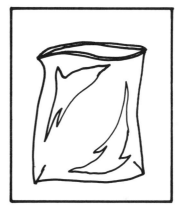

29. Communication

Name _____
Date _____
Teacher _____

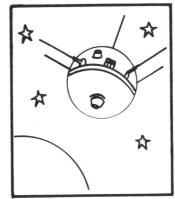

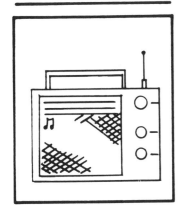

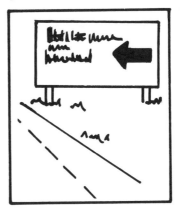

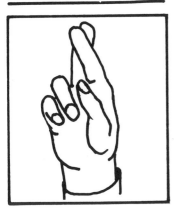

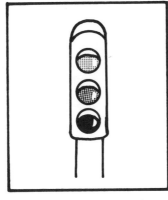

30. The Calendar

Name_____

Date_____

Teacher_____

		6	13	20	27
		5	12	19	26
		4	11	18	25
		3	10	17	24 / 31
		2	9	16	23 / 30
		1	8	15	22 / 29
			7	14	21 / 28

31. Holidays and Celebrations

32. The Map

Name_____

Date_____

Teacher_____